Press Start

Ctrl+Alt+Del
Volume 2

By Tim Buckley

www.cad-comic.com

Press Start: Ctrl+Alt+Del Volume 2

Story & Art by Tim Buckley

Type Placement and Layout by Tim Buckley

Cover colored by Xero Reynolds of www.xerjester.com

Printed in the United States of America
First Printing

Foreword and Onward

When Tim asked if I would write the introduction to his fabulous new collected work, Ctrl+Alt+Del Volume Two: Press Start, I said, "Cool. Can I write about the time we fought the slug people?"

"No."

"Okay. What about when we uncovered the time traveling Nazi plot?"

"Even if I said 'yes' it doesn't matter. We stopped it by making it never happen, there's not much to talk about, now is there."

"Yeah, I only really remember a lot of screaming anyway. What about the moleman immigration?"

"I've got an idea. Why not talk about the goddamn comic instead of blabbing about our top secret government work?"

"No, see, that's the genius of it. Haven't you heard how the best place to hide something is out in the open? We could finally talk about it because no one's stupid enough to believe it. Especially given the context. It's a webcomic collection. They'll just think I'm trying to be funny. We could even tell them what really happened to the World Trade Center."

"You know, this is why they shoved cranial bombs with remote detonators in our skulls."

"I'm almost definitely positive that they're lying to us about those."

"You really want to find out?"

"I was thinking more like you could find out."

"Hey, fuck you. Just talk about comics. Say I like Green Lantern and that's why Lucas has green eyes. No one reads the introduction anyway."

"I thought Lucas had brown eyes."

"Oh, hey, I know. Maybe you could do the introduction in your usual style? Just copy and paste someone else's introduction!"

"Words hurt, Tim. Words hurt."

"Like cranial bombs."

"I don't think you'd actually feel it."

"Just shut up and write a normal introduction."

"Hey, I could write about writing about the introduction. It'd be meta."

"You're meta."

"You don't even know what that means, do you?"

"Look, we'll talk about it later. We've got less than two minutes before we have to jump out of this plane and murder some nutjob cultists."

"Okay, okay. Man, it feels like we just did this mission too."

"Yeah, I wonder what they'll use for the cover up this time."

"Dunno, but that earthquake excuse they cooked up is starting to sound like a broken record."

"Seriously. I don't know why people actually believe in plate tectonics."

"Yeah, but I'd sleep better thinking it's that instead of the giant terraworms."

Brian Clevinger
Orlando, FL

June 8, 2005

For the fans,
who have made possible
all of this and more.

And a special thank you to
all of the video game industry
professionals who, year after year,
provide me with yummy digital
entertainment.

"ZIP IT"

HEY ETHAN?
UHH, THIS IS ROB, A NEW HIRE. I WANT YOU TO SHOW HIM AROUND WHILE I'M ON MY LUNCH BREAK.
IT WASN'T ME. IT WAS ALREADY BROKEN.
FEH.
GREAT, THANKS!
FINE. HI, I'M ETHAN. NICE TO MEET Y--
'EEEY DUDE! DO YOU LIKE VIDEO GAMES?! I'LL BET YOU DO! I LOVE FIRST-PERSON SHOOTERS! JUST LOVE 'EM!

DUDE, I HATE IT WHEN PEOPLE USE ROCKETS THOUGH CAUSE THEY'RE SO CHEAP AND YOU DON'T USE ROCKETS DO YOU? I HATE ROCKETS BUT I LOVE COUNTER-STRIKE I LOVE IT! GOTTA PLAY IT LOVE IT! WHAT ABOUT YOU, GUY?!

OK, HAVE YOU READ THE EMPLOYEE HANDBOOK YET?
NO, NOT--
GOOD! FIRST RULE IN IT IS THAT YOU DON'T TALK. EVER AGAIN.
BUT--
EVER! IT'S COMPANY POLICY.

"WELL, HERE WE GO AGAIN.

WHEN I STARTED THIS COMIC STRIP BACK IN 2002, IF YOU HAD TOLD ME THAT I'D NOW BE WORKING ON MY SECOND BOOK BECAUSE THE *FIRST* BOOK WAS SO WILDLY SUCCESSFUL, I'D PROBABLY HAVE CALLED YOU A LIAR, KICKED YOU IN THE FACE AND THEN RUN AWAY CRYING LIKE A LITTLE GIRL.

YET HERE WE ARE, WITH THE SECOND CTRL+ALT+DEL COLLECTION."

WHAT ABOUT A CO-OP ACTION GAME?
YOU **WORK** AT A GAME STORE, WITH A NICE DISCOUNT I MIGHT ADD, AND YET WE STILL DRIVE THIRTY MINUTES OUT OF OUR WAY TO SHOP HERE. EXPLAIN **THAT** ONE TO ME.

C'MON, MAN, IT'S TRADITION. WE'VE BEEN SHOPPING AT **COSMIC COMICS AND GAMES** FOR YEARS NOW. IT'S ABOUT SUPPORTING THE LITTLE GUYS.
BESIDES, I DON'T WANT TO GO TO MY STORE.
WHY NOT?

WE HIRED THIS **NEW GUY...** THIS OBNOXIOUS FANATIC. HE'S... HE'S SO... **LOUD!** AND... **ANNOYING.** AND HE'S COMPLETELY OBSESSED WITH GAMES, AND HE **NEVER** SHUTS UP ABOUT THEM! YOU HAVE NO **IDEA** WHAT IT'S LIKE TO BE AROUND THAT ALL DAY!

NO, I HAVE **NO** CLUE **WHATSOEVER** WHAT **THAT** PARTICULAR SITUATION MIGHT BE LIKE.
LET ME TELL YOU MAN, IT **SUCKS.**

"ROB WAS INTRODUCED INTO THE STRIP TO ADD A NEW DYNAMIC TO ETHAN'S WORK SITUATION. WE'VE ALL HAD TO DEAL WITH THAT PARTICULARLY ANNOYING CO-WORKER, THE ONE WHO WENT ON AND ON, AND JUST NEVER REALIZED THAT HE WAS THE MOST OBNOXIOUS PERSON ON THE PLANET.

I THINK ROB IS ONE OF THE ONLY CHARACTERS THAT IS UNIVERSALLY DESPISED BY ALL READERS, WHICH MEANS I'VE DONE MY JOB WELL."

"IN LATE SUMMER 2003 I STARTED WORK ON A CTRL+ALT+DEL COMIC BOOK, WHICH WAS GOING TO BE ALL BRAND NEW MATERIAL. I FINISHED A ROUGH SCRIPT AND STARTED PUTTING PAGES TOGETHER, BUT ENDED UP GETTING SIDETRACKED AND THE COMIC BOOK NEVER GOT FINISHED. I'VE PUT SOME OF IT ON THE NEXT PAGE FOR YOU TO TAKE A LOOK AT.

I'VE REMOVED THE DIALOGUE BECAUSE THE COMIC BOOK IS BEING REDRAWN, AND I DON'T WANT TO RUIN ANY OF THE STORY."

WARCRAFT
FROZEN THRONE
PlayStation 2
SOLD
XBOX

WARCRAFT
XBOX
HEY GUY, YOU ALRIGHT? YOU'RE LOOKIN' KIND OF *ZONED* THERE. LEMME FINISH TELLIN' YOU ABOUT THE *SNIPER!*

SLAM!
DIVE!

I'M GLAD WE WENT FOR A WALK. IT'S SUCH A BEAUTIFUL DAY.
ANY "ROB-LESS" DAY IS GREAT IN MY BOOK.

I THINK YOU MAY BE OVERREACTING ABOUT THIS. HOW BAD COULD HE BE?
WHEN HAVE I EVER OVERREACTED? FORGET I ASKED THAT. FINE. LET'S HEAD DOWN TO MY STORE, AND YOU CAN TALK TO HIM FOR A FEW MINUTES.

WAIT, DUDE! I HAVEN'T FINISHED TELLING YOU ABOUT THE NOOB CAMPER! COME BACK, GUY-- ERR, GAL!
SEE?
GET ME SOMETHING VERY SHARP. NOW!

WAIT, WAIT... IF ANYONE GETS TO KILL HIM, IT'S GOING TO BE ME.
KILL HIM?! WHO CARES ABOUT HIM?! I NEED TO GOUGE OUT MY EARDRUMS TO PREVENT THEM FROM EVER BEING VIOLATED IN SUCH A WAY AGAIN!

"I USUALLY ASSUME THAT ETHAN IS BLOWING THINGS OUT OF PROPORTION, BUT THAT ROB GUY IS EASILY THE MOST OBNOXIOUS HUMAN BEING I HAVE EVER BEEN IN THE SAME ROOM WITH."

"I HAVE A COMPLAINT"

I NEED YOU TO CALL WORK FOR ME. PRETEND YOU'RE A CUSTOMER AND COMPLAIN ABOUT ROB. SAY HE GRABBED YOUR ASS OR SOMETHING.
NO.
WHY NOT?
I'M NOT GOING TO HELP YOU GET SOME GUY FIRED. MAKE THE CALL YOURSELF.
I TRIED BUT I CAN'T DO IT WITHOUT LAUGHING MANIACALLY.
1337 CHEF

PERHAPS YOU SHOULD JUST GO HAVE A TALK WITH THIS GUY. MAYBE YOU CAN LEARN TO TOLERATE HIM.
FINE, DON'T HELP. I'LL DO THIS *MY* WAY. DO WE HAVE AN *ANVIL?* WE MUST. WHERE DO WE KEEP IT?
IN THE LIVING ROOM, ON THE SHELF... RIGHT NEXT TO YOUR SANITY.
1337 CHEF

"SINCE THIS STRIP CAME OUT, I REGULARLY GET REQUESTS TO CREATE A '1337 CHEF' APRON FOR OUR ONLINE STORE.

WHO KNEW THERE WERE SO MANY GAMERS THAT LIKED TO COOK?"

"IT'S TRUE"

CHEF BRIAN SAYS:
A ROBERT SMITH FROM OHIO WRITES:
"DEAR CHEF BRIAN, I WAS CURIOUS WHY IT DOESN'T SNOW IN THE SUMMER."
"IT WOULD REALLY HELP COOL THINGS DOWN."

WELL, BOBBY...
PANCAAAAAAAAAAAAAAAAKE.

SHINK!

SQUIRT

"OW. MY BRAIN."

OH GREAT MERCIFUL CRAP-SHIT!
A DAISY TASTY!
BUTTERFLY MARSHMALLOW SUPREME!

I WRITE TO YOU, FEELING THE *BURNING* OF HOT PICKLES IN MY HEART.
AND SO I TRANSCRIBE THE MELODIES OF LOVE AND SNOW-TIRES WITH MY CHEESE-FRIEND DONUT PENCIL.
BLUE *GOOSE,* MI AMOR...

WARCRAFT 3: FROZEN THRONE
WHOEVER AT B-B-BLIZZARD B-B-BRAINSTORMED THIS FUCKING IDEA CAN B-B-BITE MY FROZEN ASS!
THIS CHAIR SUCKS!

"WHENEVER PEOPLE ASK ME WHAT MY LEAST FAVORITE STRIP THAT I'VE DONE IS, I IMMEDIATELY NAME THIS ONE. I DON'T THINK IT'S HORRIBLE, OR IT NEVER WOULD HAVE BEEN POSTED IN THE FIRST PLACE. THERE'S JUST SOMETHING ABOUT IT THAT BUGS ME."

"SWEET EMBRACE"

OK, SO IT'S JUST THE THREE BOXES TODAY. IF YOU COULD JUST SIGN--
STOP! DO YOU HEAR IT? DO YOU FEEL IT?!

HEAR WHAT? I DON'T HEAR A DAMNED THING...
IT'S AS IF THE THOUSANDS OF VOICES IN MY HEAD ALL CRIED OUT IN JOY, AND THEN WERE SUDDENLY SATISFIED...
A GREAT DISTURBANCE IN THE FORCE...

LISTEN, MAN, I DON'T THINK--
SHH!

A-HA!
CRUNCH!

"AFTER MY FIRST CONVENTION, I REALIZED THAT A LITTLE HAND-DRAWN PENCIL AND INK SIGN ON THE FRONT OF MY TABLE JUST WASN'T GOING TO CUT IT.

AFTER THAT I STARTED HAVING LARGE BANNERS PRINTED UP FOR CONVENTIONS, STARTING WITH THE FIRST ONE I DID FOR OTAKON 2003, WHICH YOU CAN SEE ON THE NEXT PAGE."

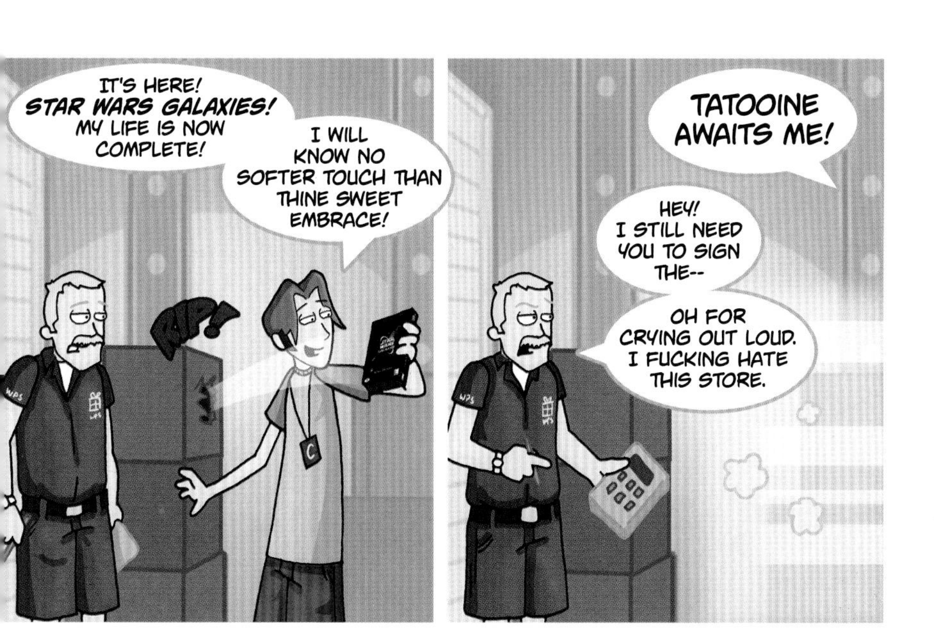
IT'S HERE!
STAR WARS GALAXIES!
MY LIFE IS NOW COMPLETE!
I WILL KNOW NO SOFTER TOUCH THAN THINE SWEET EMBRACE!
RIP!
TATOOINE AWAITS ME!
HEY! I STILL NEED YOU TO SIGN THE--
OH FOR CRYING OUT LOUD. I FUCKING HATE THIS STORE.

CTRL+ALT+DEL
at
otakon 2003
AN ANIME CONVENTION? I'M NOT SURE WE BELONG HERE...
DON'T BE RIDICULOUS. WE PLAY VIDEO GAMES. VIDEO GAMES COME FROM JAPAN. ANIME COMES FROM JAPAN.
IT'S THE SAME THING. NOW GO DRESS AS SOMETHING 'CHIBI'.
WWW.CAD-COMIC.COM

"IN THE END"

REMOVING STAR WARS GALAXIES... PLEASE WAIT...
SNIFFLE SO MUCH POTENTIAL... SO MUCH...
SO... GOING TO KILL YOURSELF THEN?
GALAXIES SUCKED. I NO LONGER SEE THE POINT IN LIVING.
ISN'T KNIGHTS OF THE OLD REPUBLIC COMING OUT SOON?

WELL... IT WOULD BE A SHAME TO WASTE A PERFECTLY GOOD NOOSE. WANT TO HELP ME FIND TED?
I NEED TO LEARN TO KEEP MY MOUTH SHUT.
REMEMBER... HE'S SLIPPERY. BUT HOW FAST CAN HE BE ON THOSE STUBBY LITTLE FLIPPERS? JUST YELL IF YOU SEE HIM.

"STAR WARS GALAXIES WAS THE PRETTIEST AND MOST ELABORATE DAMNED *CHAT ROOM* THAT I'VE EVER SEEN."

"INDECISION"

PLAYED IT, PLAYED IT, BEAT IT, PLAYED IT-- OH...
MORROWIND... THAT WAS SUPPOSED TO BE PRETTY GOOD. I NEVER REALLY GOT INTO IT...

OK, LOOKS LIKE WE'RE READY TO GO HERE... LET'S FIRE THIS BABY UP.
HMM... MY CHARACTER NAME? OH... UMM... LET'S SEE... UHH.. HOW ABOUT... HMM...

HMM...
HMM...
YOU'VE BEEN ON THE COMPUTER FOR SIX HOURS AND YOU HAVEN'T EVEN CHOSEN A NAME YET?
YOU CAN'T RUSH THESE THINGS! THE NAME IS THE BASIS OF YOUR WHOLE CHARACTER!
IN THAT CASE NAME HIM 'SAMANTHA'. THAT FITS YOU LIKE A GLOVE.

"NAMING MY CHARACTER IS ALWAYS THE HARDEST PART ABOUT RPG'S FOR ME, ***ESPECIALLY*** MASSIVELY MULTIPLAYER ONES. ONCE YOU CHOOSE A NAME, YOU'RE STUCK WITH IT FOR THE ENTIRE LIFE OF YOUR CHARACTER. YOUR NAME REFLECTS YOUR IDENTITY. YOU CAN'T JUST CHOOSE A NAME LIKE "BILL" AND EXPECT PEOPLE TO TAKE YOUR ELVEN WARRIOR SERIOUSLY. OF COURSE, CERTAIN PEOPLE WITHOUT BRAINS GET AROUND THIS DILEMMA BY USING SUCH GENIUS NAMES AS 'LEGULAS' OR 'L3GOLAS'..."

"RIDING IN STYLE"

SO WHAT'S THIS BIG OL' INSECT THING? CAN I *KILL* IT?

THESE ARE CALLED *SILT STRIDERS.* WE USE THEM FOR TRANSPORTATION HERE IN MORROWIND.

WELL, IF IT GETS ME AROUND FASTER THAN WALKING, I'M GAME. ALL I HAVE ARE THESE *GOLD COINS...* IS THAT ENOUGH?
I'M *SURE* WE CAN WORK SOMETHING OUT.

WE HOLLOW OUT AN AREA IN THE CREATURE'S *CARAPACE* FOR OUR PASSENGERS TO RIDE IN!
SPLOOSH!

OK, WELL... MAYBE IT'S NOT *ENTIRELY* HOLLOWED OUT. THE INTESTINES ACTUALLY MAKE FOR COMFORTABLE SEATING THOUGH.
EWW...

"IF YOU'RE INTO MASSIVE RPGS, AND DON'T REQUIRE SOME SORT OF ONLINE COMMUNITY TO ENJOY THEM, ELDER SCROLLS: MORROWIND IS RIGHT UP YOUR ALLEY. I'VE NEVER PLAYED A GRAPHICAL RPG THAT WAS QUITE AS VAST AS MORROWIND.

IF YOU HAVE THE OPTION, I WOULD RECOMMEND PICKING IT UP FOR THE PC. THERE IS SUCH A WEALTH OF COMMUNITY-MADE MODS FOR THE GAME, IT EXTENDS THE PLAY-TIME BY *MONTHS.*"

ETHAN, CAN I ASK YOU A QUESTION?
SQUEE SQUEE
OF COURSE. YOU CAN ASK ME ANYTHING.
DO YOU WATCH PORN?
CRASSHHH!
HOW CAN YOU ASK ME THAT?!
THERE'S NO WAY I CAN ANSWER!
IF I SAY YES, YOU'LL GET UPSET!
IF I SAY NO, AND YOU FIND OUT I'M LYING, YOU'LL GET UPSET!
SO... THAT'S A YES.
NO!
SO IT'S A NO?
YES!
I MEAN NO!!
FUCK!

"I THINK MOST OF US GIRLS KNOW THAT *EVERYONE* WATCHES PORN SOMETIMES. WE JUST REALLY LIKE TO WATCH GUYS SQUIRM WHEN WE ASK."

CHEF BRIAN SAYS:
IT'S A FAIRLY COMMON MISCONCEPTION THAT YOU CAN'T MAKE WINDOWS OUT OF BRICK.
MOST PEOPLE FEEL THAT BRICK IS TOO SOGGY. I ASSURE YOU, IT IS A SHOE.

SCIENTISTS HAVE DISCOVERED THAT NINE OUT OF TEN SHOES ARE NUMB. THIS BRINGS UP THE DISTURBING QUESTION:
DOES COFFEE BLEED?

IF IN FACT IT DOES, THEN ONE MUST CONSIDER THE POSSIBILITY THAT ALL LIFE IS BUT A GIANT CAKE MOLD.
BUT INSTEAD OF DELICIOUS, GOOEY CAKE BATTER, WE ARE FILLED WITH...
RAISINS.

THUMP

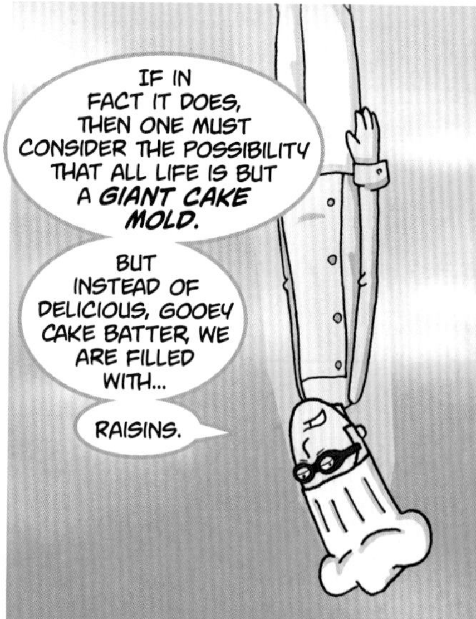

"THE NUMBER ONE QUESTION THAT I HAVE BEEN ASKED MOST FREQUENTLY SINCE I STARTED THIS WEBCOMIC IS "WHERE DID CHEF BRIAN COME FROM?" I HAVE NEVER DONE A CONVENTION WHERE I DIDN'T GET ASKED THIS AT LEAST TWICE. ONCE I GOT ASKED SIX TIMES DURING THE SAME PANEL.

...

IF YOU'RE WAITING FOR AN ANSWER, GO BUY THE FIRST BOOK."

ARE YOU SWEEPING?
WELL SOMEONE HAS TO. YOU'VE BEEN PLAYING MORROWIND NON-STOP.
YEAH... IT'S BEEN A WHILE SINCE I'VE FOUND SUCH AN INVOLVING RPG.

YOU PLAYED FOR THREE DAYS STR-- AUUGHH!!
WHAT?! WHAT IS IT?!
WHAT THE HELL IS ON YOUR FACE?!

THWACK!

IS IT DEAD? HOLD STILL AND I'LL KILL IT.
NO NO... NO. I ASSURE YOU, IT IS QUITE DEAD, THANK YOU.

"ETHAN CAN GO WEEKS WITHOUT SHAVING AND END UP WITH NOTHING MORE THAN A FEW LITTLE WHISKERS.

MAYBE THAT WILL CHANGE ONCE HE HITS PUBERTY."

WHAT IF?
AND NOW WE MUST FIGHT! GOOD VERSUS EVIL! LIGHT VERSUS DARK!
KSSH
YEAH, THAT'S *USUALLY* HOW IT WORKS.

KSSH NOW YOU WILL DIE!
BRING IT, **BITCH.**
VSSHHH

VSSHHH

KSSH DID YOU HAVE THE LIGHTSABER TURNED AROUND **BACKWARDS?** *KSSH*
NO!
KSSH **YES** YOU DID. I CAN **SEE** IT. IT WENT RIGHT THROUGH YOU.
I'M GONNA NEED A MINUTE HERE.

"OBVIOUSLY ONE WOULD HOPE THAT A JEDI WOULD BE SKILLED ENOUGH TO NOT MIX UP THE ENDS OF HIS LIGHTSABER. THEY ARE PRETTY CYLINDRICAL, AND IT WOULD BE AN EASY MISTAKE TO MAKE... BUT THEY'RE *JEDI*...

BUT THE POSSIBILITY IS WHY I STARTED DOING 'WHAT IF?' STRIPS. TO DATE THEY'VE ALL BEEN STAR WARS RELATED, BUT I'LL USE THEM FOR ANY MOVIES, IF THE RIGHT IDEA STRIKES ME."

"BEACHED"

HEY, IT'S A GREAT DAY OUT. LET'S HEAD TO THE BEACH.
THE... THE BEACH?

NO WAY, MAN! PEOPLE DIE AT THE BEACH! I'M NOT GOING TO GET IN THE MIDDLE OF FLYING BULLETS AND MORTAR EXPLOSIONS JUST SO YOU CAN GET A TAN!

WHAT THE HELL ARE YOU TALKING ABOUT?!

ETHAN, NOT ALL BEACHES ARE LIKE THE NORMANDY BEACH INVASION LEVEL IN MEDAL OF HONOR!
UH HUH. THAT SOUNDS LIKE SOMETHING AN AXIS SPY WOULD SAY. ARE YOU AN AXIS SPY, LUCAS?

"GETTING ETHAN TO DO ANYTHING THAT INVOLVES BEING OUTSIDE AND AWAY FROM SOME SORT OF ELECTRONIC ENTERTAINMENT DEVICE IS NOTHING SHORT OF A MIRACLE.

IF I WANT HIM TO GO TO THE BEACH WITH ME, I HAVE TO REMIND HIM THAT I'LL BE WEARING A BIKINI."

"NATURAL LIGHT", EH?
I'M NOT SO SURE ABOUT THIS...
ETHAN! STOP BEING SUCH A WUSS! THE WATER IS GREAT!
DO I DARE INFLICT THIS ON MY DELICATE IRISH COMPLEXION?

SCREW IT. I WANT TO GO SWIMMING.

HISSSSSSSSSSSSSSS

FUCKING... OW...
DON'T FORGET SOME SUNBLOCK!
YOU CAN BLOCK THAT THING?!

"QUICK NOD TO THE *METROID* SWIM SHORTS.

THAT'S RIGHT, BABY. THAT'S HOW *I* ROLL."

G'MORNING. SO THEN... HOW WAS THE BEACH, MAN?
I HAD A GREAT TIME.
BUT ETHAN DID NOT?
HE TOLD YOU?

WELL, IT'S NOT SO MUCH THAT HE ***TOLD*** ME, AS THAT I HEARD HIM SOBBING LIKE A LITTLE GIRL WHILE HE WAS GETTING DRESSED THIS MORNING.
YEAH, HE GOT A PRETTY NASTY SUNBURN.

SO HOW DID YOU EVEN GET HIM THERE IN THE FIRST PLACE?
HEH, I TOLD HIM IT WOULD BE JUST LIKE ***DOA BEACH VOLLEYBALL.***

HE DIDN'T FLIP OUT WHEN HE REALIZED YOU LIED?
ACTUALLY... IT ***WAS*** JUST LIKE DEAD OR ALIVE VOLLEYBALL.
I NEED TO GO TO THE BEACH MORE OFTEN...

"I HAD BEEN OCCASIONALLY USING THE 'COLORED LINES' TECHNIQUE HERE AND THERE, MOSTLY ON INANIMATE OBJECTS AND BACKGROUNDS. I DECIDED TO ATTEMPT IT ON A FULL COMIC STRIP TO SEE HOW I, AND THE READERS, LIKED IT.

RESPONSE WAS MIXED. I LIKE THE STYLE, BUT NOT NECESSARILY FOR CTRL+ALT+DEL. I DECIDED TO STICK WITH THE TRADITIONAL BLACK LINES, AND SAVE THIS TECHNIQUE FOR FUTURE PROJECTS..."

MAN, I WANT TO PLAY MY GAMECUBE, BUT THAT MEANS I WOULD HAVE TO GET UP AND WALK ALL THE WAY OVER THERE TO SWITCH THE CONSOLE.
TOO MUCH WORK.

I'VE GOT IT!
USING MY INCREDIBLE TECHNICAL EXPERTISE, I WILL COMBINE BOTH SYSTEMS INTO ONE SUPER SYSTEM THAT WILL PLAY ALL GAMES!
I MUST FETCH MY TOOLS!

FIVE MINUTES LATER...
EXCUSE ME!

ETHAN! WHY IS THE COUCH ON FIRE?! DEAR GOD!
IN THE CLOSET, EVERYTHING GOES AWAY.

"I JUST NEED A MIDGET. MY VERY OWN MIDGET WHOSE SOLE PURPOSE IT IS TO GET UP AND CHANGE THE CHANNEL, OR SWAP VIDEO GAME DISCS, OR GET ME A DRINK FROM THE FRIDGE.

IF I HAD MY OWN MIDGET I COULD BE LAZY IN THE WAY I WAS TRULY INTENDED TO BE."

"BUILT TO LAST"

SO YOU'VE DESTROYED OUR COUCH. I HOPE YOU'RE HAPPY.
I DON'T THINK IT'S NEARLY AS BAD AS IT LOOKS.

WHAT ARE YOU TALKING ABOUT? IT'S TOAST.
CRISPIFIED.
THIS COUCH HAS SURVIVED MORE HARD TIMES THAN WE CAN COUNT. SHE'S A TOUGH OL' GAL...
PAT PAT

PAT
FWOOSH

TO ASHES! TO ASHES! NOW WHO WILL CRADLE MY REAR END FOR MARATHON AFTER MARATHON OF GAMING AND ANIME SWEETNESS?!

YOU ARE SO CLEANING THIS UP.
WHO, I ASK?! WHO?!

"DESTROYING THE COUCH, FOR ME AT LEAST, WAS SOMEWHAT SYMBOLIC. THE COUCH REPRESENTED THE HUMBLE BEGINNINGS OF THE COMIC, AND THE OLD 'TWO GAMERS ON A COUCH' CLICHE, WHICH CTRL+ALT+DEL WAS RAPIDLY MOVING BEYOND.

AND ON A MUCH LESS METAPHORICAL LEVEL, DESTROYING SUCH AN INTRINSIC PART OF A GAMER'S LIFESTYLE JUST MAKES FOR GOOD HUMOR."

"SAYING GOODBYE"

IT FEELS LIKE I HARDLY KNEW YOU, AND NOW YOU ARE **GONE...**
IN THE BLINK OF A EYE, A LIFE IS SNUFFED OUT.
ALL TOO YOUNG AND NAIVE OF THE JOYS LIFE HAS TO OFFER.
JOYS YOU WILL NEVER KNOW...

YOU BEGAN YOUR LIFE AS A SERVANT...
AN OBJECT FOR SITTING AND SLEEPING... AND PERHAPS DECORATION.
BUT SOON YOU BECAME A PARTNER... A FRIEND... A **LOVED ONE.**
I CAN ONLY HOPE IT WAS YOUR WISH TO BE CREMATED.
I NOW COMMIT YOUR BODY TO A PLACE THAT I FEEL SYMBOLIZES YOUR EXISTENCE.
I THINK IT'S WHAT YOU WOULD HAVE WANTED...

ETHAN! ACK! THBBTT! WHY DID YOU DUMP **ASH** ALL OVER THE SALES FLOOR?!

SHUSH! A MOMENT OF SILENCE FOR THE DEARLY DEPARTED.
PlayStation 2

"AS WITH THE POSTERS ON THE WALLS OF THE APARTMENT, THE GAMES ON THE SHELVES OF GAMEHAVEN (THE VIDEO GAME STORE WHERE ETHAN WORKS) ARE ALWAYS TITLES THAT I AM CURRENTLY PLAYING, OR HAVE RECENTLY ENJOYED, OR SOMETIMES JUST ONES I'M REALLY LOOKING FORWARD TO.

I DON'T GET PAID TO ADVERTISE THESE THINGS, IT'S JUST A LITTLE EXTRA THAT I ADD TO THE COMICS."

"KICK BACK AND RELAX"

FRANKLY I'M A BIT SURPRISED WITH YOU.
HEY, HOW ABOUT THIS ONE? IT'S ALMOST EXACTLY LIKE OUR OLD COUCH.
HUH?
SHE'S HARDLY BEEN GONE A DAY AND ALREADY YOU'RE MOVING ON.

I DON'T UNDERSTAND HOW YOU CAN EVEN THINK ABOUT REPLACING--
HOLY FREAKING CRAP! WHAT IS THAT?!

RECLINERS? DON'T YOU THINK THAT'S A BIT TOO... TELEVISION SITCOM-ISH?
WHAT?! IT RECLINES TOO?! IS THAT WHAT THIS BUTTON IS FOR?

PWONG!

"CTRL+ALT+DEL WILL ALWAYS HAVE A HEALTHY DOSE OF SLAPSTICK HUMOR. I GREW UP ON ***TOM AND JERRY,*** AND SATURDAY MORNING CARTOONS, AND IT'S A TYPE OF HUMOR I REALLY ENJOY WRITING, AS WELL AS WATCHING."

SO HOW ARE THINGS WITH YOU AND LILAH?
OH MAN, IT'S ***INCREDIBLE.***
YEAH?
EVIL DEAD

DEFINITELY.
SHE'S SUPPORTIVE, AND WARM, AND COMFORTING...
AND SHE MOLDS TO MY ASS LIKE ***NOBODY'S*** BUSINESS!
EVIL DEAD

EVIL DEAD

I SAID 'HOW ARE THINGS WITH YOU AND ***LILAH***'.
OH! ***LILAH!*** HEH, I THOUGHT YOU SAID ***RECLINER.***
EVIL DEAD

"I WAS INTRODUCED TO THE EVIL DEAD SERIES WAY OUT OF ORDER. I FIRST SAW EVIL DEAD 2, FOLLOWED BY ARMY OF DARKNESS. I WAS IMMEDIATELY A FAN OF THE SERIES, AND AFTER MONTHS OF KEEPING AN EYE OUT, I FINALLY FOUND A PLACE THAT HAD THE ORIGINAL EVIL DEAD.

IF YOU'RE A FAN OF THE FILMS, YOU SHOULD READ 'IF CHINS COULD KILL', BY BRUCE CAMPBELL."

HEY, LINUX-BOY. CARE TO PARTAKE OF OUR NEW SEATERY?
UHH... I GUESS SO?

GO AHEAD AND PICK UP A CONTROLLER. LET'S PLAY A FEW ROUNDS.
I'M NOT MUCH OF A GAMER... BUT ALRIGHT.
MIND IF I SNEAK IN A QUICK MEDITATION BEFORE WE START?

WHAT IS THAT? SOME OF THAT "NEW AGE HIPPIE" SHIT?
I FIND IT HELPS ME FOCUS WHEN TRYING NEW THINGS.
HEY, WHATEVER FLOATS YOUR BOAT.

LAAAAAAAME.

"IN LATE SUMMER OF 2003 I RELEASED THE VERY FIRST OFFICIAL CAD T-SHIRTS, NOT COUNTING THE CAFE PRESS DESIGNS FROM A WHILE BACK. THEY CONSISTED OF A CHARACTER ON THE FRONT, AND A QUOTE ON THE BACK. THERE WERE FIVE DESIGNS TO BEGIN WITH, ETHAN, LUCAS, LILAH, CHEF BRIAN AND TED. THEY WERE AVAILABLE IN BLUE, GREEN AND BLACK.

THEY HAVE SINCE BEEN REPLACED WITH UPDATED DESIGNS, BUT ON THE NEXT PAGE YOU CAN SEE THE ORIGINAL T-SHIRT ARTWORK."

OK, I'M READY. TRY TO GO EASY ON ME.
YOU'RE PLAYER TWO.
LET THE ASSKICKING BEGI--
ROUND ONE... FIGH-- PLAYER TWO **WINS!**

WOW, THE EXECUTION OF THIS WHOLE "VIDEO GAME" CONCEPT IS EASIER THAN I THOUGHT...

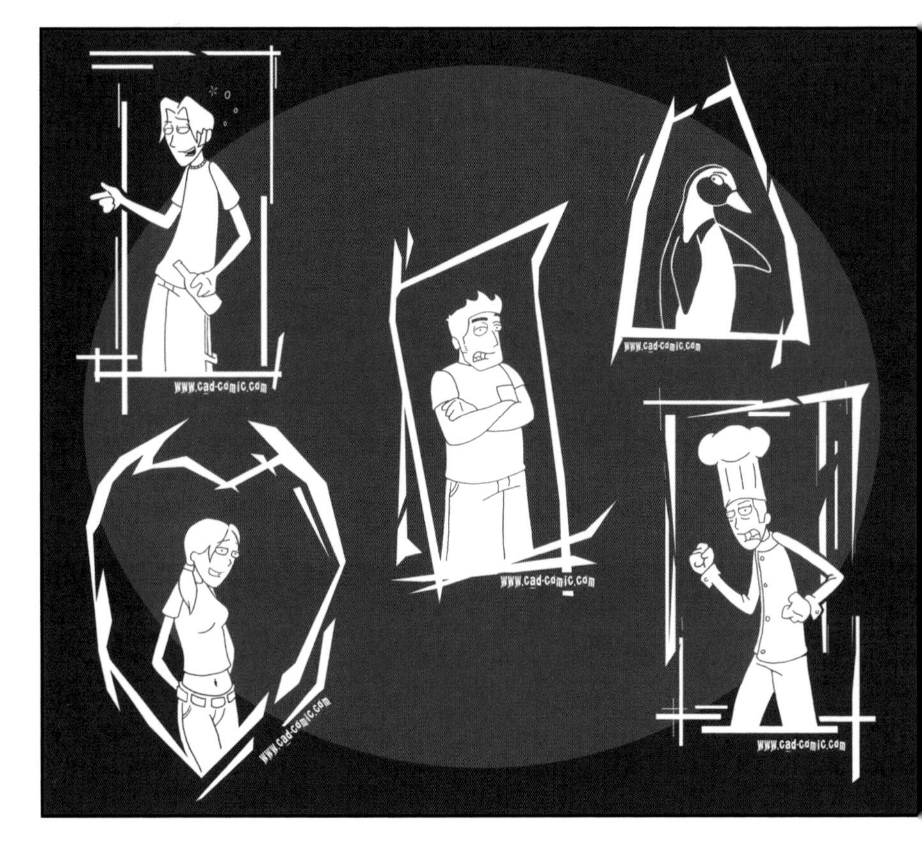
www.cad-comic.com
www.cad-comic.com
www.cad-comic.com
www.cad-comic.com
www.cad-comic.com

PLEASE! PLEASE TEACH ME MEDIMATATION, SCOTT!
ETHAN, MEDITATION IS NOT A MAGIC TRICK. IT IS A SOUL SEARCHING TOOL.

IT TAKES YEARS TO TRULY MASTER THE ART.
I'M NOT GOING TO TEACH YOU JUST BECAUSE YOU WANT TO WIN VIDEO GAMES.

PLEASE SCOTT! I WANT TO LEARN THE WAYS OF THE FORCE!
I WANT TO BECOME A JEDI, LIKE MY FATHER BEFORE ME!

I MIGHT ACTUALLY LIKE TO SEE THE EFFECT OF MEDITATION ON A BROKEN PSYCHE...
SCREW YOU OBI-WAN! YOU'RE ALWAYS HOLDING ME BACK!

"MEDITATION IS DESCRIBED AS 'CONTINUOUS AND PROFOUND CONTEMPLATION OR MUSING ON A SUBJECT OR SERIES OF SUBJECTS OF A DEEP OR ABSTRUSE NATURE'."

Meditation Station
Techniques for the Mind, Body and Soul
NOW I WANT EVERYONE TO TAKE A DEEP BREATH... HOLD IT... AND RELAX.
DOES ANYONE HAVE ANY QUESTIONS SO FAR?
YES, ETHAN?
YEAH, WHEN DO WE LEARN HOW TO CHANNEL OWNAGE INTO VIDEO GAMES?
FOR THE LAST TIME, THAT IS NOT COVERED IN THIS CLASS!
EVERYONE CLOSE YOUR EYES AND FOCUS ON YOUR BREATHING.
I WANT YOU TO STEP FORWARD NOW... STEP FORWARD INTO YOUR CAVE...
AND THERE YOU WILL FIND YOUR...
SLIDE?

"THIS IS THE ONLY TIME TED HAS EVER 'SPOKEN'".

I CAN FEEL THE POWER COURSING THROUGH ME!
ONCE THE APPRENTICE, NOW *I* AM THE MASTER!
WITH MEDITATION I WILL DOMINATE EVERY GAME I PLAY!
NO ONE WILL STAND IN MY WAY!
OUT OF MY WAY, KID!
DARK SIDE POINTS!
SHOVE!
I MUST FIND A GAME WITH WHICH TO TEST MY NEWFOUND POWER!
BUT WHERE TO START...
ETHAN, DUDE! I'M GLAD YOU'RE HERE! I WANTED TO TELL YOU ABOUT THIS *COUNTER-STRIKE* MOD THAT--
SILENCE, MORTAL! ONE COPY OF *KNIGHTS OF THE OLD REPUBLIC,* AND BE QUICK ABOUT IT!

"THIS IS PROBABLY ONE OF THE MORE COMPLEX STORYLINES I HAD DONE TO THIS POINT. STARTING OFF WITH THE DESTRUCTION OF THE ICONIC COUCH, LEADING INTO FURTHER ESTABLISHING SCOTT'S 'FREE-THINKING' PERSONALITY, COMPLETE WITH A STAR WARS AND FIGHT CLUB REFERENCE AND EVEN INCORPORATING THE RECENT RELEASE OF ***KNIGHTS OF THE OLD REPUBLIC.***

PRETTY CRAZY, HUH?"

HEY ETHAN, GUESS WHA- EEP!
DIE! **DIE** 'TILL YOU'RE DEAD! DIE DIE DIE **DIE!**

SO... WHAT THE HELL?
I FEAR ETHAN HAS BECOME CORRUPTED.
I WARNED HIM OF THE DANGERS OF MEDITATION...
HIS REASONS FOR LEARNING THE ART WERE UNPURE.
THE DESIRE FOR GAMING "LEETNESS" HAS CONSUMED HIM.
IS THERE ANYTHING WE CAN DO?
JUST LET HIM BE. HIS POWER WILL EVENTUALLY DESTROY HIM FROM THE INSIDE OUT.
OR... I COULD KNOCK SOME SENSE INTO HIM... I *SUPPOSE.*
UHH...
YEH.

"ALTHOUGH MANY PEOPLE WOULD CLASSIFY CTRL+ALT+DEL AS A 'GAMING COMIC', I LIKE TO THINK OF IT AS MORE OF A ***GAMER*** COMIC. I DO JOKES ABOUT VIDEO GAMES, BUT THE MAJORITY OF THE HUMOR IS ABOUT THE GAMERS THEMSELVES."

"NOT EXACTLY EPIC"

ETHAN, THIS ENDS NOW.
YOU'RE JEALOUS THAT I'VE GROWN MORE POWERFUL THAN YOU!

ETHAN...
MEDITATION CAN BE USED FOR SO MUCH MORE THAN RELAXATION!
LIKE WHORING YOUR OPPONENTS IN VIDEO GAMES!
ONLY I HAVE THE COURAGE TO SEE THAT!
YOU FEAR THE POWER, WHILE I SEE ITS POTENTIAL!

ETHAN, YOU ARE MISGUIDED. LET ME HELP YOU.
THERE IS ONLY ONE WAY TO RESOLVE THIS, AND YOU KNOW IT.
SO BE IT.

GOOD ALWAYS PREVAILS.
PFFT. NOOB.

"I'VE ALWAYS BEEN ADAMANT THAT WORD BALLOONS AND TEXT ARE JUST AS MUCH A PART OF THE ARTWORK AS THE PANELS THEMSELVES.

SINCE THERE IS ONLY SO MUCH I COULD DO TO VISUALLY CONVEY ETHAN'S DESCENT TO THE DARK SIDE, IN THIS CASE I USED COLORED WORD BALLOONS TO FURTHER DISPLAY ETHAN'S GROWING EVILNESS."

YOU HAVE BEEN DEFEATED. WHAT DO YOU HAVE TO SAY FOR YOURSELF?
YOU WIN! NO MORE! PLEASE, NO MORE!

I SEE NOW THAT MY MIND WAS CLOUDED BY A DESIRE TO BE A GAMING GOD.
I FINALLY REALIZE THAT TRUE MASTERY OF MEDITATION TAKES YEARS.
I WAS WRONG, AND I AM ASHAMED.

YOU'VE HAD A ROUGH FEW DAYS. YOU SHOULD GET SOME REST.
I HOPE YOU'VE TRULY LEARNED YOUR LESSON.
I HAVE...

OH YES... I'VE LEARNED. I'VE LEARNED VERY WELL...
AND NEXT TIME YOU WON'T BE SO LUCKY... NO... NO YOU WON'T...
MUAHAHA HAHAHAHAHA! HAHAHAHAH HAHA!
DID YOU SAY SOMETHING, ETHAN?
UHH... NOPE. NOT A THING.

"AFTER I HAD SO MUCH FUN AT *CONNECTICON* IN JULY OF 2003, I IMMEDIATELY WANTED MORE. I FOUND OUT THERE WAS A LARGE CONVENTION DOWN IN BALTIMORE CALLED ***OTAKON.*** IT WAS ONLY A WEEK LATER, SO THERE WASN'T MUCH TIME TO PREPARE, BUT I HASTILY MADE ARRANGEMENTS TO ATTEND. OTAKON WAS MY FIRST EXPOSURE TO A REALLY LARGE CONVENTION, AND DESPITE STILL BEING A SMALLER WEBCOMIC AT THE TIME, A LOT OF PEOPLE CAME OUT TO SAY HELLO."

"OTAKON 2003 SPECIAL EDITION"
ON THE BUS RIDE TO BALTIMORE, I DISCOVERED THAT SOME PEOPLE AREN'T SATISFIED WITH JUST LISTENING TO THEIR HEADPHONES.
NO, NO, NO. THEY HAVE TO SING ALONG TOO. LOUDLY. OFF-KEY. PAINFULLY.
BALTIMORE WAS A NICE CITY.
GIMME A DOLLAR OR I'LL CUT YOUR NUTS OFF!
NEED FOOD
I'VE ALWAYS LIKED CITIES.
DESPITE THE OVERWHELMING TRAFFIC AT THE CONVENTION, I ONLY HAD TO BEAT ONE PERSON TO DEATH.
MY PEOPLE SKILLS ARE IMPROVING.
THE PEOPLE I STAYED WITH WERE REALLY NICE.
TIM, YOU'RE SPILLING ALCOHOL ALL OVER YOURSELF!
I'M JUSHT... MARKING MY... MY... *TERRITORY!*
HEY RED! YOU SUCK! BLUE RULES!
CHUPA-THINGY! I *LIKE* IT! IT'S GOT A RING TO IT!
WE GOT DRUNK AND PLAYED SOME HALO.
I MET PONTUS MADSEN OF *LITTLE GAMERS.*
DUDE, YOUR COUNTRY IS FUCKED UP.
SOB I KNOW! I KNOW!
SNIFFLE THANKS FOR THE SHIRT...
HE GAVE ME A T-SHIRT.
THE RIDE HOME WAS UNPLEASANT THANKS TO THE *'BUS NAZI'*.
YOU *SIT* WHERE I GOD-DAMNED *TELL* YOU TO SIT!
"NO SEAT FOR ME!"

"THESE ARE A BUNCH OF SKETCHES THAT I DID WHILE I WAS DOWN IN BALTIMORE, AND I TURNED THEM INTO A SORT OF SUMMARY FOR THE TRIP, TO ACCOMPANY THE LONG-WINDED CONVENTION REPORTS I USUALLY WRITE.

THIS IS THE ONLY CAD STRIP THAT ISN'T COLORED, AND IT'S THE ONLY TIME I'VE EVER DONE A CONVENTION COMIC STRIP."

HOW TO SOLVE A PROBLEM IN KNIGHTS OF THE OLD REPUBLIC...
I COULD PROBABLY FURTHER INVESTIGATE THIS MATTER FOR YOU...
BUT I'M A JEDI, SO I'M ALWAYS RIGHT NO MATTER WHAT.
THE JEDI CONSULAR WAY

OK, SEE THIS DOUBLE-BLADED LIGHTSABER?
YOU HAVE UNTIL BOTH ENDS ARE LIT TO STOP YOUR CHILDISH BICKERING.
THE JEDI GUARDIAN WAY

NO, I DON'T CARE ABOUT YOUR STUPID PROBLEM!
BUT NOW I'M GOING TO KILL YOU JUST FOR ASKING!
THE DARK SIDE (ASSHOLE) WAY

MONKEY SWEET POTATO! MY HAT!
THE CHEF BRIAN WAY

"KNIGHTS OF THE OLD REPUBLIC WAS ONE OF MY FAVORITE GAMES OF 2003, BUT IRONICALLY I DIDN'T ACTUALLY BEAT IT UNTIL MID-2004. THAT HAPPENS QUITE OFTEN. I START PLAYING A GAME, BUT THEN A NEW GAME COMES OUT, OR WORK GETS REALLY BUSY, AND I GET DISTRACTED. THE GOOD GAMES I USUALLY END UP GOING BACK TO AT A LATER DATE AND FINISHING.

AND I WENT EVIL, MOST DEFINITELY. DARK SIDE REPRESENT!"

SO THERE'S A LOT OF HYPE SURROUNDING XIII. WHAT CAN YOU TELL ME ABOUT THE WORK GOING INTO THE GAME?
WELL OUR STAFF HAS BEEN WORKING DILIGENTLY TO PUSH THE ENVELOPE OF GAME DESIGN AND PRODUCE THE BEST GAME THAT WE CAN.
STAFF
OUR TEAM OF DEDICATED CODERS AND GRAPHIC ARTISTS--
SCREEEEEE!
STAFF
SLAM!
STAFF
THAT WASN'T A MONKEY...
HEY, WHAT ARE YOU WRITING? HEY...
YOU'RE NOT ALLOWED TO WRITE HERE. IT'S... UH... A 'NO WRITING' ZONE.
LAST CHANCE TO PUT DOWN THE PEN...

"THERE WAS A PARTICULARLY LARGE HYPE MACHINE WORKING AROUND THIS GAME XIII (THIRTEEN), A CELL-SHADED FIRST PERSON SHOOTER. I PLAYED A DEMO FOR IT, AND I WASN'T IMPRESSED AT ALL."

"IS THAT THE MEDICAL TERM?"

HEY, GUESS WHAT?
THEY INVENTED A WHEELCHAIR THAT CAN GO UP STAIRS.
STAIRS!
I DON'T CARE.

NOW THERE IS NO PLACE A WHEELCHAIR CAN NOT ACCESS...
THAT'S A GOOD THING, ETHAN.
I WANT ONE.

ETHAN, YOU AREN'T DISABLED.

AHEM. I AM A GAMER. BY NATURE I SUFFER FROM LAZINESS. I DON'T JUST ***WANT*** ONE OF THOSE CHAIRS. I ***DESERVE*** ONE.

THEY'LL NEVER GIVE YOU ONE...

OH, I BEG TO DIFFER.

I HAVE DETERMINED THAT YOU SUFFER FROM A SEVERE CASE OF STUPIDITY.
HOWEVER, THAT DOES NOT QUALIFY AS A DISABILITY.
NOW PLEASE GET OUT OF MY OFFICE.
I WANT A SECOND OPINION, YOU HACK!

"JUST TO FURTHER PROVE THAT I DRAW INSPIRATION FROM EVERY ASPECT OF LIFE, THIS COMIC CAME ABOUT AFTER I WAS BROWSING THE NEWS AND READ THE AFOREMENTIONED ARTICLE ABOUT A WHEELCHAIR THAT COULD CLIMB STAIRS.

WELL, MY GEARS STARTED TURNING AND PRETTY SOON I HAD TWISTED IT INTO ANOTHER ONE OF ETHAN'S CRAZY SCHEMES."

"THE CAUSE OF IT ALL"

WHY?! WHY, WHY, WHY?!
WHY DO COMPANIES INSIST ON RELEASING CRAPPY GAMES LIKE THIS?
IT BOGGLES THE MIND!

THINK OF ALL THE WASTED HOURS IN DEVELOPMENT AND PRODUCTION TO CREATE SUCH... MEDIOCRITY!
THIS GAME IS HORRIBLE! IT DOESN'T EVEN DESERVE THE MINIMAL EFFORT IT WOULD TAKE FOR ME TO COME UP WITH A CLEVER INSULT FOR IT!

SHITTY VIDEO GAMES ARE SOLELY RESPONSIBLE FOR THE PROBLEMS IN THIS WORLD... LIKE GLOBAL WARMING!

HUNGER EPIDEMICS!

LIGHT BEER!

A PLAGUE UPON OUR SOCIETY!

ARE YOU FINISHED YET?
OH NO, MY FRIEND! THIS IS JUST THE BEGINNING!
WONDERFUL.

"CRAPPY VIDEO GAMES ARE A PET PEEVE OF MINE. NOW OBVIOUSLY NOT EVERY SINGLE GAME CAN BE A HALO, OR A HALF-LIFE, BUT THERE IS NO EXCUSE FOR SOME OF THE TRULY HORRIBLE GAMES THAT HIT THE SHELVES. AND I'M TALKING ABOUT HORRIBLE AS IN SUB PAR GRAPHICS, BAD CONTROLS, CAMERA ISSUES, GLITCHES, ETC. GAMES THAT JUST LACK ANY DISPLAY OF EFFORT. IT MOST OFTEN APPLIES TO GAMES BASED ON MOVIE AND TELEVISION LICENSES, BUT CAN AFFLICT ANY GAME."

"MOVING UP THE LADDER"

CUSTOMER SUPPORT, HOW MAY I HELP YOU?
HELLO, I WAS JUST CALLING TO POLITELY AND CALMLY TELL YOU THAT YOUR GAME SUCKS THE FAT ASS!
JUST A MOMENT... LET ME TRANSFER YOU TO MY SUPERVISOR.

HELLO SIR, WHAT SEEMS TO BE THE PROBLEM?
OH, THERE'S NOT MUCH OF A PROBLEM, UNLESS YOU WERE TO COUNT THE FACT THAT YOUR GAME SUCKS PREPOSTEROUS AMOUNTS OF THE ASS!
ONE SECOND SIR, AND I'LL GET MY MANAGER ON THE LINE.

HOW CAN I ASSIST YOU, SIR?
OK, PERHAPS YOU ARE THE ONE I NEED TO TALK TO ABOUT YOUR GAME BEING THE BIGGEST SUCKER OF SUCKING, EVER!
PLEASE STAY ON THE LINE WHILE I TRANSFER YOU TO THE HEAD OF PUBLIC RELATIONS.

THREE HOURS LATER...
GAME DEVELOPMENT, WHAT'S UP?
GAME! SUCK! THE ASS!
HEY, SCREW YOU BUDDY. GO MAKE YOUR OWN DAMNED GAME THEN.
SUCKS THE-- HEY! YOU KNOW WHAT?! I WILL!
BY THE WAY, YOU SUCK!

"IT'S IMPORTANT TO REMEMBER THAT WHEN DEALING WITH CUSTOMER SERVICE, OVER THE PHONE OR IN PERSON, THAT PERSISTENCE, STUBBORNNESS, PATIENCE AND A HEALTHY DOSE OF ALCOHOL WILL ALWAYS GET YOU WERE YOU WANT TO BE.

AS A CUSTOMER YOU ARE ALWAYS RIGHT. OF COURSE, THAT'S COMPLETE BULLSHIT, BUT IF THE CUSTOMER SERVICE REPRESENTATIVES ARE FORCE-FED IT, WHO ARE WE TO ARGUE?"

SONUVA...
LUCAS! THERE YOU ARE!
I'VE BEEN LOOKING FOR YOU!

YOU NEED TO START BUILDING A GRAPHICS ENGINE.
OH I DO, HUH?
WE'RE GOING TO MAKE OUR OWN VIDEO GAME. THE BEST GAME EVER!

THINK OF IT, LUCAS! YOU AND I AT THE HELM OF OUR OWN GAME STUDIO!
IT'S NOT ONLY OUR RIGHT AS GAMERS, BUT OUR DESTINY!

ETHAN, MAKING A VIDEO GAME IS A LOT OF HARD WORK.
MOST OF WHICH YOU'LL BE DOING.
AND I'M OK WITH THAT.

"AFTER THE SUCCESS OF THE FIRST T-SHIRT DESIGNS, I QUIT MY JOB IN SEPTEMBER OF 2003 AND OFFICIALLY BECAME A FULL-TIME WEB COMIC ARTIST. IT WAS PRETTY SCARY AT FIRST, BEING SELF-EMPLOYED, BUT HERE I AM YEARS LATER AND STILL GOING STRONG. I HAVE MY READERS TO THANK FOR THE COURAGE TO TAKE THE LEAP OF FAITH AND DO WHAT I LOVE FOR A LIVING."

"FALSE PRETENSES"

THANK YOU ALL FOR COMING. LILAH **WOULD** BE HERE, BUT SHE WAS WATCHING THE ***FINAL FANTASY X2*** TRAILER ON REPEAT...
LILAH?
AND SHE THREW SOME HEAVY OBJECTS AT MY HEAD WHEN I TRIED TO TURN IT OFF.

I HAVE INVITED YOU ALL HERE TODAY BECAUSE I HAVE A VISION! A DREAM!
WHO IS LILAH?
AND EACH OF YOU PLAY A PART IN MAKING THAT DREAM A REALITY...

OK, I LIED. I ONLY INVITED TED HERE SO I COULD TEST OUT THE ACCURACY OF THIS NEW CROSSBOW.
WHAT?! TED? CROSSBOW?! NOT GROOVY!
WHAT KIND OF LUNATIC WOULD SELL ***YOU*** A WEAPON?!

"PENGUINS ARE BIRDS, BUT THEY CAN'T FLY. NOT IN THE AIR AT LEAST. PENGUINS WILL ACTUALLY SPEND UP TO SEVENTY-FIVE PERCENT OF THEIR TIME IN THE WATER.

IF TED ISN'T IN THE REFRIGERATOR COOLING DOWN, I OFTEN FIND HIM SWIMMING AROUND IN THE BATHTUB. THE WAY HE FLAPS HIS LITTLE WINGS IT... ALMOST LOOKS LIKE HE'S FLYING."

SO... YOU MISSED THE FIRST DEVELOPMENT MEETING.
YEAH, SORRY ABOUT THAT. FINAL FANTASY, Y'KNOW?
DID THINGS GO WELL?
WELL, LUCAS PICKED UP SOME BOOKS ON BUILDING A GRAPHICS ENGINE, SO HE'S WORKING ON THAT.
I CAN TAKE CARE OF TEXTURES AND CONCEPT ART. AND OF COURSE, MANAGING THE PROJECT.
SCOTT IS PRETTY MUCH USELESS, BUT I'LL HAVE HIM DO SOME WRITING AND WEB PAGE WORK.
WHO IS DOING THE MODELS?
MODELS?
YEAH, YOU KNOW... **MODELS.** THE GROUPS OF POLYGONS THAT YOU PUT YOUR TEXTURES ON?
PRETTY MUCH EVERYTHING **VISUAL** IN A GAME?
OOOOH... THOSE DON'T **COME WITH** THE GRAPHICS ENGINE?
WHAT ABOUT IF I LEAVE A VIDEO CARD UNDER MY PILLOW? WILL THE **GRAPHICS FAIRY** BRING ME MODELS?
ETHAN... SOMETIMES YOU **FRIGHTEN** ME A BIT...

"ETHAN ALWAYS PUTS THINGS UNDER HIS PILLOW EXPECTING SOME MAGICAL FAIRY TO BRING HIM SOMETHING BETTER.

THE WORST WAS PROBABLY WHEN HE DECIDED HE WANTED TO OWN AN ICE CREAM FACTORY AND PUT A BANANA-SPLIT SUNDAE UNDER HIS PILLOW..."

AND SO THE GAME IS COMING ALONG, BUT NOW I FIND OUT I NEED A MODELER.
I SUPPOSE I COULD LEARN TO MODEL, BUT IT WOULD TAKE FOREVER.

I DON'T WANT TO RECRUIT ONLINE, EITHER.
I NEED MY TEAM CLOSE BY SO THAT I MAY THREATEN THEM WITH VIOLENCE IN ORDER TO *MOTIVATE* THEM.
AND DEFINITELY NO SPRITES. PIXELS MAY BE CLASSIC, BUT THEY ARE TOO LIMITING.

AS YOU CAN SEE, I'M FACED WITH QUITE THE DILEMMA.
I'LL REQUIRE A COPY OF *F-ZERO GX* FREE OF CHARGE IN ORDER TO HELP ME SORT IT ALL OUT...
NO.
BUT... THE DILEMMA, BARRY. THE DILEMMA.

DUDE! ETHAN! HEY, GUY! I OVERHEARD YOUR CONVERSATION! I MAKE MODELS FOR COUNTER-STRIKE ALL THE TIME, DUDE! CAN I BE ON YOUR TEAM?!
IRONY... WE MEET AGAIN, YOU CRUEL, SADISTIC ***BITCH***.

"BEFORE I EVER STARTED CTRL+ALT+DEL, I USED TO BE PRETTY ACTIVE IN THE MODDING COMMUNITY AS A SKINNER. MY MOST PROMINENT WORK WAS ON JEDI KNIGHT 2: JEDI OUTCAST, WHERE I WORKED WITH A TALENTED MODELER AND FRIEND TO CREATE THE FIRST BOBA FETT AND JANGO FETT MODELS FOR THE GAME, AMONG OTHERS.

I ALSO DID SOME TEXTURE WORK ON AN INDEPENDENT MMORPG."

OK, HOW GOOD CAN ROB'S MODELS POSSIBLY BE?
THERE IS NO WAY THAT SOMEONE AS OBNOXIOUS AS HIM WOULD HAVE ANY TALENT WORTH MENTIONING.
NO, THEY'LL BE TERRIBLE. THEY WILL BE TERRIBLE AND I WILL HATE HIM EVEN MORE FOR WASTING MY TIME.
BUT... BUT WHAT IF THEY'RE GOOD?
WELL, IF THEY TURN OUT TO BE GOOD, I CAN ALWAYS RUN MY FACE THROUGH A CIRCULAR SAW TO AVOID HAVING TO LET HIM WORK ON THE VIDEO GAME PROJECT.
POWER TOOLS ALWAYS PROVIDE A WAY OUT OF ANY SITUATION.

HEHE, THESE ARE GOING TO BE SUCH CRAP. THEY--
OH WOW.
THAT'S A COMPUTER MODEL?
THE DETAIL...
THEY... WOW...
WOW!
CRAP...
FUCK...

CRAPFUCK!!

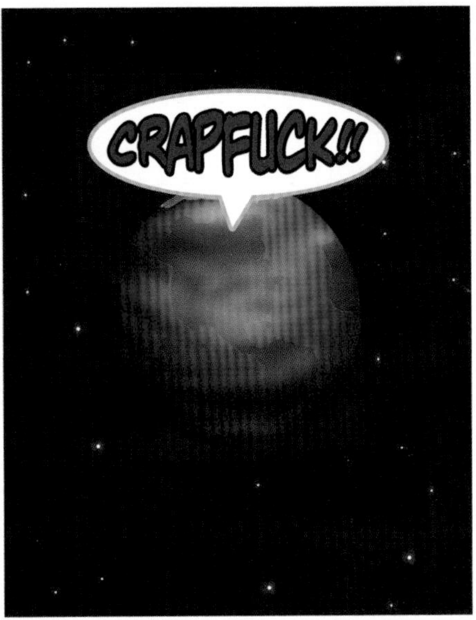

"ON SECOND THOUGHT, I THINK IT WOULD WORK OUT BETTER FOR ALL PARTIES INVOLVED IF ROB WERE THE ONE TO HAVE AN 'UNFORTUNATE ACCIDENT' WITH A VERY LARGE DRILL BIT."

"COLLARED"

NOW THAT YOU'RE ON THE TEAM, I'LL NEED YOU TO WEAR THIS ATTRACTIVE COLLAR...
UHH...
ANY TIME YOU DISOBEY A DIRECT ORDER, IT WILL EMIT A SMALL, NON-FATAL ELECTRICAL CHARGE...

THEY ALWAYS RUN...
HEY, WAS THAT THE REALLY ANNOYING GUY THAT YOU WORK WITH? HE'S NOT WORKING ON THE VIDEO GAME PROJECT, IS HE?
NO WAY, I REFUSE TO WORK WITH THAT GUY.

I GOT YOU THIS ATTRACTIVE ***NECKLACE...***
SWEETIE, I WILL HIT YOU ***SO*** HARD...

"SOMEWHERE IN THE GOLDEN GLOW OF THE JELLY SANDWICH, A DELIVERY MAN IS WEEPING.
IT OCCURS TO ME THAT THE DELIVERY MUST HAVE BEEN SOME NATURE OF GHASTLY... WHAT? WHAT'S THAT YOU SAY? POTATO SHOES?
WELL I AGREE."

"AMBITIOUS DESIGNS"
HERE IS THE PRELIMINARY SYNOPSIS FOR OUR GAME. THIS IS CHAPTER ONE, PART A, SUB-SECTION ALPHA. IT'S FOUR HUNDRED PAGES, SO YOU'LL WANT TO START READING RIGHT AWAY.
OH... *GREAT.*
I'VE DECIDED AGAINST STICKING TO ANY ONE GENRE. WE DON'T WANT TO LIMIT OURSELVES.
INSTEAD OUR GAME WILL CREATE A NEW GENRE, ONE TO ENCOMPASS ALL EXISTING GENRES.
ACTION, ADVENTURE, RPG, RACING, SIM, FPS, RTS, FIGHTING, SPORTS...
WE WILL USE THEM *ALL.*
THE MORE WE ADD, THE BETTER OUR CHANCES OF SUCCESS!
OUR GAME WILL BREAK EVERY BOUNDARY!
DAMN, THIS IS HEAVY. HOW MUCH MORE IS THERE?
I'M STILL WORKING ON DEFINING *L337* AS A GENRE.
THIS GAME IS STARTING TO SMELL LIKE A *DAIKATANA...*

"'LEETSPEAK' ACTUALLY ANNOYS THE HELL OUT OF ME.

I FIND IT FUNNY IN A 'DAMN, THAT'S PRETTY STUPID' SORT OF WAY, NOT IN A 'OMGZORZ!!1! IT IS 2 COOL DOOD!' WAY.

SOME OF THE SIMPLER FORMS OF LEETSPEAK ARE TOLERABLE, LIKE REPLACING A COUPLE OF LETTERS WITH NUMBERS, BUT CONSTRUCTING EVERY WORD OUT OF SYMBOLS IS JUST AWFUL."

HEY ROB, HOW ARE THOSE MODELS COMING ALONG?
DUDE... WHAT MODELS, GUY? YOU HAVEN'T DESIGNED ANYTHING FOR ME TO MODEL YET...
I'M NOT LOOKING FOR EXCUSES, ROB. SEE, THIS IS WHY WE NEED THE COLLARS.
YOU'RE--
RUNNING THIS PROJECT, REMEMBER?
DO I HAVE TO DO EVERYTHING? A LITTLE SELF-MOTIVATION WON'T KILL YOU. A LITTLE AMBITION.
YOU DON'T NEED GAMEPLAY OR DESIGN TO CREATE PRETTY GRAPHICS, ROB.
JUST TAKE A LOOK AT STAR WARS GALAXIES...
BUT DUDE, IN COUNTER-STRIKE WE ALWAYS--
THIS ISN'T COUNTER-STRIKE, ROB.
COUNTER-STRIKE IS LIKE PONG COMPARED TO OUR GAME. EXCEPT THAT PONG, UNLIKE COUNTER-STRIKE, IS STILL COOL.

"*THIS* IS EXACTLY WHAT I'M TALKING ABOUT. UNLESS YOU SUSPEND YOUR EMPLOYEES OVER A TANK FILLED WITH FLESH-EATING PIRANHAS, THEY'LL NEVER BE MOTIVATED ENOUGH TO MEET DEADLINES."

"NEED FOR SPEED"

WORKING ON OUR GAME ENGINE?
YEAH, I THINK I'VE COME UP WITH SOME REALLY INVENTIVE IDEAS, HERE.
The Return of the Great Adventure.

HAVE YOU THOUGHT ABOUT... MAYBE... WORKING FASTER?
YEAH. AND THEN I STARTED THINKING ABOUT HITTING YOU REALLY, REALLY HARD.

WHAT ABOUT AN EXPLOSIVE DEVICE STRAPPED TO YOUR CHAIR THAT WAS SET TO EXPLODE IF YOU TYPED BELOW ONE HUNDRED WORDS PER MINUTE...
PERHAPS THAT WOULD MOTIVATE YOU?
RAIDERS

ACTUALLY, YOU KNOW WHAT WOULD SPEED THINGS UP? IF YOU SAT DOWN AND HELPED ME CODE...
WHOA, LET'S NOT GET HASTY. THAT'S HOW ACCIDENTS HAPPEN.

"SOMEHOW I THINK IT'S POSSIBLE THAT ETHAN IS PHYSICALLY ALLERGIC TO ANYTHING THAT MIGHT BE CONSTRUED AS REAL, TIME-CONSUMING WORK.

HE BREAKS OUT IN EXCUSES."

"HANDS ON

ICING YOUR HANDS?
YEAH, TOO MUCH **CODING.** BUT IT'S COMING ALONG WELL.
Fletch

LISTEN, I WAS JUST READING CHAPTER 42, PART M, APPENDIX 29 OF ETHAN'S GAME PROPOSAL...
INTERESTING AND FRIGHTENING ALL AT THE SAME TIME, ISN'T IT?
Fletch

YEAH. HE LISTS PAGES AND PAGES OF GAMES TO USE FOR REFERENCE.

"THE STEALTH SYSTEMS OF ***METAL GEAR*** AND ***SPLINTER CELL*** COMBINED WITH ACTION LIKE ***MAX PAYNE.***

ALSO INCLUDE RPG ELEMENTS SUCH AS THOSE FOUND IN DEUS EX AND KNIGHTS OF THE OLD REPUBLIC..."

HE EVEN CITES THE POPULARITY OF ***DANCE DANCE REVOLUTION*** AND SUGGESTS WE "WORK IT IN".

LUCAS, IS THIS PROJECT EVEN ***POSSIBLE?***
IT HAD BETTER BE, BECAUSE I DON'T WANT TO LISTEN TO ETHAN BITCH IF IT ISN'T.
ALSO, I THINK I ALREADY HAVE ***CARPAL TUNNEL...***
Fletch

"FLETCH! AWESOME MOVIE.

CHEVY CHASE, DAN AYKROYD, BILL MURRAY, JOHN CANDY, MARTIN SHORT. THESE WERE THE COMEDIC GENIUSES OF THE EIGHTIES AND EARLY NINETIES.

ALSO CHECK OUT 'SPIES LIKE US', 'CADDYSHACK', AND 'NOTHING BUT TROUBLE'."

FINALLY! IT TOOK ME THE BETTER PART OF THE LAST FEW WEEKS, BUT I FINISHED THE GRAPHICS ENGINE!
PFFT. TOOK YOU LONG ENOUGH.
COLDPLAY

I'VE BEEN SO BUSY CODING, I HAVEN'T EVEN CHECKED OUT ANY OF THE CONCEPT ARTWORK FOR THE GAME. CAN I SEE SOME? I'M ANXIOUS TO SEE WHAT THE GAME IS LOOKING LIKE.
WELL I **COULD** SHOW YOU...
COLDPLAY

EXCEPT IT DOESN'T EXIST. SINCE... I HAVEN'T DRAWN ANY YET.
WHICH MIGHT EXPLAIN WHY ROB HASN'T FINISHED ANY MODELS YET...
WHAT?
OR... **STARTED** ANY, FOR THAT MATTER.
COLDPLAY

ETHAN, I SWEAR, IF MY HANDS WEREN'T NUMB FROM TYPING...
YOU'D GO DOWNLOAD SOME PORN. SPARE ME THE DETAILS.
SO, UH... HOW ABOUT THE WEATHER LATELY? OR... LET'S TALK ABOUT SPORTS TEAMS AND HOW THEY ARE DOING... UHH...
OLDPLAY

"BEFORE GOING UP ON THE WEBSITE, THE COMICS GET SHRUNKEN DOWN ABOUT FOUR TIMES THEIR ORIGINAL PRODUCTION SIZE."

HE'S BEEN CRACKING THE WHIP AT *US* THIS WHOLE TIME, AND HE HASN'T BEEN DOING ANY WORK HIMSELF!
YEAH... BUT IS IT REALLY THAT BIG OF A DEAL, THOUGH?
BY ITSELF, NO. BUT THIS IS JUST TYPICAL OF ETHAN AND IT'S REALLY DAMNED FRUSTRATING! THIS *ALWAYS* HAPPENS.
AND I WAS *JUST* GETTING EXCITED ABOUT THIS PROJECT, TOO. I WOULD DO THE ART MYSELF, BUT I'M NOWHERE NEAR AS GOOD AN ARTIST.

WELL, HE **DID** WRITE THAT CONCEPT OUTLINE. IT LOOKED LIKE HE PUT A LOT OF TIME INTO THAT...

YEAH, FIFTY CHAPTERS. ***NINETY PERCENT*** OF WHICH WAS HIM REMINDING US WHAT WOULD CATCH FIRE IF WE DIDN'T WORK.

HE'S MY BEST FRIEND, AND I DON'T WANT TO BE ANGRY AT HIM, BUT IT JUST... JUST... ***COOKS MY CHICKEN!***

ARGH! I'M SO FRUSTRATED I CAN'T EVEN CURSE PROPERLY.

DAMNIT, ***NOW*** I'M PISSED.

"THE THREAT OF FIRE FOR NOT WORKING IS SORT OF A MOOT POINT, SINCE WHEN ETHAN IS AROUND THINGS CATCH ON FIRE REGARDLESS OF WHAT ANYONE ELSE IS DOING."

ETHAN, LUCAS SAYS-- UHH... WHY ARE YOU WEARING A TIE?
IT MAKES ME LOOK MORE PROFESSIONAL. SOME PEOPLE ARE FORGETTING WHO IS IN CHARGE OF THIS PROJECT.
UMM... YEAH...
LISTEN, LUCAS WAS JUST A LITTLE FRUSTRATED. YOU SHOULD GO TALK TO HIM.
HE NEVER STOPPED TO CONSIDER THAT I WAS BUSY WITH OTHER OBLIGATIONS!
SOMEONE HAS TO PLAY SOUL CALIBUR 2 AROUND HERE! IT'S NOT GOING TO PLAY ITSELF!
C'MON ETHAN! DON'T BE STUBBORN! JUST GO MAKE AMENDS.
NOPE, NOT UNTIL HE APOLOGIZES FOR TURNING ME INTO A RHINOCEROS WHILE I SLEPT.
ETHAN... HE DIDN'T TURN YOU INTO A RHINOCEROS. STOP MAKING EXCUSES.
HEY BABY... JUST 'CAUSE YOU DIDN'T SEE IT, DOESN'T MEAN IT DIDN'T HAPPEN.

"IN ORDER TO ADVANCE YOUR ARTWORK, YOU HAVE TO ALWAYS BE TRYING NEW THINGS. WITH THIS STRIP I BEGAN DRAWING CTRL+ALT+DEL A LITTLE BIT DIFFERENTLY, USING DIFFERENT MATERIALS AND TECHNIQUES WITH THE GOAL OF ACHIEVING A MORE DYNAMIC AND UPDATED LOOK TO THE CHARACTERS. IT'S ALL PART OF THE CONTINUAL GROWTH OF THE ARTWORK THAT YOU CAN SEE FROM THE FIRST STRIP TO THE LATEST."

"HOLD THAT TONGUE"

ALRIGHT ETHAN. I'M **SORRY** THAT I GOT ANGRY AT YOU.
THAT'S RIGHT. SPIT IT OUT. BOW DOWN TO THE TIE, **BITCH.**

I'LL EVEN LET **THAT** COMMENT SLIDE. LET'S JUST GET BACK TO THE PROJECT, OK? EVERYTHING COOL?
THE TIE IS FOREVER... THE TIE--
WHAT? OH, YEAH. WE'RE COOL.

GOOD. LET'S JUST HAVE FUN WITH IT. I MEAN, IT'S NOT LIKE ANYONE EXPECTS THE PROJECT TO REALLY SUCCEED, RIGHT?

TWITCH!

I MEAN... UHH... WHAT I MEANT WAS... I DIDN'T MEAN--

BASTARD! YOU HEATHEN! YOU **NON-BELIEVER!** YOU'RE OFF THE TEAM! **OFF** I SAY!

"2 OUNCES SHREDDED BEEF-CARROT
4 CUPS DEGRADATION
A PINCH OF WAX FROM AN ALMOND-SCENTED CANDLE
1 TBSP PAVEMENT

MIX THOROUGHLY AND BRING TO A SIMMER ON A STOVETOP, STIRRING REGULARLY WITH A DECEASED OR UNCONSCIOUS REPTILE."

YOU'RE WEARING A TIE TO WORK NOW? THAT'S... INTERESTING.
ACTUALLY I PUT IT ON AND NOW THE KNOT WON'T COME UNDONE...

ANYWAY! LUCAS IS OUT OF THE PICTURE! KAPUT! FINITO! ROB, YOU'RE MY NEW BEST FRIEND.
DUDE, THAT'S AWESOME, GUY! WE CAN PLAY COUNTER-STRIKE AND HANG OUT ALL THE TIME, DUDE!

ON SECOND THOUGHT, I'D RATHER SWALLOW A MOUTHFUL OF ANGRY BEES.
BARRY, YOU'RE MY NEW BEST FRIEND.
WHOA, I AGREE TO NOTHING!

"CTRL+ALT+DEL FANS HAVE LATCHED ONTO SOME PRETTY OUTRAGEOUS THINGS ABOUT THIS COMIC, BUT DURING THIS STORYLINE THERE WAS ACTUALLY A 'RED TIE FAN CLUB'.

THEY WANTED ME TO MAKE THE RED TIE A MAIN CHARACTER. THEY MADE FORUM ICONS, RED TIE FAN ART, AND EVEN SENT IN PICTURES OF THEMSELVES WEARING RED TIES."

"FULL CIRCLE"

I WONDER IF KICKING LUCAS OFF OF THE TEAM WAS THE RIGHT THING TO DO...
HE'S BEEN MY BEST FRIEND FOR... WELL FOREVER. AND HE *DID* PUT A LOT OF WORK INTO THAT ENGINE...
WAS I TOO HARSH?

BUT ON THE OTHER HAND, HE *DID* DISRESPECT THE PROJECT.
NO NO, HE DISRESPECTED THE TIE!
THE TIE!
NO ONE SPEAKS ILL OF THE TIE!
WE DON'T NEED HIM!

AND YET... I MISS TALKING TO HIM.
WE'VE BEEN FRIENDS FOR SO LONG... IT'S STRANGE NOT SPEAKING TO HIM...
IT'S A HUGE ADJUSTMENT FOR ME...

BUT I'LL GET THROUGH IT...
WITH THE HELP OF MY NEW *BEST FRIEND!*

"THIS WAS THE 200TH CTRL+ALT+DEL STRIP, AND TO MARK THE OCCASION I HAD SCRIPTED THIS STORYLINE TO RE-INTRODUCE THE MELON ON THIS EXACT OCCASION. ONE OF THE MOST FREQUENTLY ASKED QUESTIONS I WOULD GET AT THE TIME WAS 'WHAT HAPPENED TO THE MELON?', SO WITH THIS STRIP I GAVE A SILENT NOD TO MY HUMBLE BEGINNINGS, AND SORT OF BROUGHT EVERYTHING FULL CIRCLE."

LOOK AT THIS... THIS IS A DISGRACE! I'M COMPLETELY SCHOOLING YOU.
AT LEAST BLOCK OR SOMETHING... SIDESTEP, PARRY, WHATEVER. I MEAN, I KNOW I'M A SOUL CALIBUR 2 MASTER AND ALL, BUT AT LEAST PRETEND TO PUT UP A FIGHT.
HEY... WAIT A MINUTE... YOU'RE NOT LETTING ME WIN, ARE YOU?! LUCAS WOULD NEVER HAVE LET ME WIN...
I DON'T NEED YOUR CHARITY.
THE TIE IS GOING TO BE VERY UPSET WITH YOU IF YOU'RE LETTING US WIN...

DON'T GIVE ME THAT LOOK! I DID TEACH YOU HOW TO PLAY!
YOU HAVE NO ONE BUT YOURSELF TO BLAME!
LOOK! LOOK! I'M KICKING YOU! JUST DO... SOMETHING!
HIT ME BACK!

PRESS THE B BUTTON! BLOCK! BLOOOOCK! GAAAH!
MAYBE YOU SHOULD GO HAVE A CHAT WITH HIM..
WHAT, AND ROB OURSELVES OF THIS WHOLESOME ENTERTAINMENT?

"MAXI FOR THE WIN.

FUCK THAT MITSURUGI PUNK.
GIVE ME THE PIRATE WITH THE NUNCHAKU ANY DAY."

SO NOW THAT WE'RE EVEN MORE SHORT-HANDED ON THIS PROJECT, WHAT IS OUR NEXT STEP?
WHAT? OH, RIGHT. YOU DON'T KNOW YET.
WHAT DO I NOT KNOW?
YOUR SERVICES ARE NO LONGER NEEDED. NONE OF YOU ARE NEEDED. WE'LL TAKE OVER FROM HERE.
"WE"?

YES. AND WE'VE INVITED THE MELON TO WORK ON THE PROJECT WITH US.
HAVE YOU MET THE MELON?
WE'RE CALLING HIM ***RUPERT*** NOW.
ETHAN, LISTEN TO ME ***VERY*** CAREFULLY... RUPERT IS A ***FRUIT.***
HEY, NOW. I KNOW YOU MAY BE BITTER ABOUT YOUR REMOVAL FROM THE TEAM, BUT RUPERT'S SEXUAL PREFERENCE IS HIS ***OWN*** BUSINESS.

"I THINK THAT MOST GIRLS WOULDN'T TOLERATE BEING REPLACED BY A MELON.

BUT YOU JUST HAVE TO UNDERSTAND, ETHAN ISN'T TRYING TO BE HURTFUL... HE'S JUST AN IDIOT."

"GRAND THEFT MELON"

MAYBE IF WE GET THAT WATERMELON AWAY FROM HIM... MAYBE *THEN* HE'LL SNAP OUT OF IT.
HE'S ALWAYS GOT IT WITH HIM THOUGH.
I MAY HAVE A PLAN...

ETHAN!
I'VE GOT NOTHING TO SAY TO YOU.
DEAR GOD, YOUR *XBOX* IS ON *FIRE!*

WHAT?!
HANG IN THERE, BABY! PAPA'S COMIN'!!
YOINK!

"YOINK"? WHAT--
EEEEEEEK!
RUPERT!
MELON THEFT! *MELON THEFT!*

"I THINK IN SOME COUNTRIES IT'S AGAINST THE LAW TO EVEN *JOKE* ABOUT A MAN'S VIDEO GAME CONSOLE BEING IN PERIL."

ALRIGHT, WHERE IS HE?! SHE! IT!
COME AGAIN?
MY MELON! WHERE IS IT?!

WELL I'M NOT SURE, ETHAN. WHERE DID YOU LEAVE IT LAST?
YOU'RE WELCOME TO SOME OF MY MELON IF YOU'D LIKE...
DO NOT TRY TO DISTRACT ME WITH DELICIOUS FRUITS! I WANT TO KNOW WHERE--

MARK MY WORDS... RUPERT WILL BE AVENGED.
ACTUALLY I THINK RUPERT WILL BE FRUIT SALAD...

"ALONG WITH EVERYTHING ELSE, EVEN MY WORKSPACE WHERE I CREATE THE COMIC HAS GROWN OVER TIME. FROM THE HUMBLE BEGINNINGS PENCILING THE COMIC AT A KITCHEN TABLE AND COLORING IT ON A SINGLE COMPUTER IN MY BEDROOM, TO WORKING AT A DRAFTING TABLE AND A DUAL WORKSTATION IN THE CTRL+ALT+DEL OFFICE."

I WAS MISTAKEN... IT WASN'T THE MELON. I WAS SURE HE'D SNAP OUT OF IT...
MAYBE IT'S THE--
OF COURSE! HOW COULD I BE SO BLIND?! THE TIE! THE TIE IS THE SOURCE OF ETHAN'S MADNESS!
UHH...
ERR... THIS TIME. THE TIE IS THE SOURCE OF ETHAN'S MADNESS THIS TIME.
WHAT DO YOU PROPOSE?
TONIGHT... WHILE HE SLEEPS. WE SOLVE THIS PROBLEM ONCE AND FOR ALL...
INSERT DIABOLICAL LAUGHTER HERE, RIGHT?

"AFTER A WHILE YOU HAVE TO WONDER WHY YOU WOULD BOTHER KEEP TRYING TO KEEP ETHAN'S SANITY TETHERED TO REALITY.

JUST TURN HIM OVER TO SCIENCE FOR RESEARCH, I SAY."

CREEAAK

TIE!
CRACK!

LUCAS?!
NO NO... THERE IS NO TALKING... THERE IS ONLY PAIN.

"IT ALSO KEEPS ME SAFE FROM THE PS2 MONSTERS UNDER MY BED."

UGH...
WHO THE HELL SLEEPS WITH AN XBOX, ANYWAY?
IT'S MY BINKY...
THE EXORCIST

AND WHAT WERE YOU DOING SNEAKING INTO MY ROOM IN THE--
HURK!
GIMME THAT.

THE XORCIST

NOOOOO TIIIIIEEEEEEEEEE!! AUUUGHHH!
AHHHHH!
THE XORCIST

"I HAD BEEN TOYING AROUND WITH A NEW COMIC STRIP WHERE ALL OF THE MAIN CHARACTERS WERE ROBOTS. I FELT THERE WERE A LOT OF OPPORTUNITIES FOR HUMOR WHERE ROBOTS WERE INVOLVED, BUT DUE TO TIME CONSTRAINTS AND HOW BUSY CTRL+ALT+DEL WAS KEEPING ME, I NEVER REALLY GOT THE STRIP OFF THE GROUND.

ON THE NEXT PAGE YOU CAN SEE ONE OF THE CHARACTER DESIGNS AND AN UNFINISHED PAGE. SEE ANYTHING FAMILIAR?"

CAN'T BREATHE! LUNGS DEFLATING!
ETHAN.
EYEBALLS! MY EYEBALLS ARE BURNING!
ETHAN.
GETTING WEAK... GETTING... SO VERY... WEAK...
ETHAN!
WHAT?!
KNOCK IT OFF.
EXCUSE ME, A LITTLE FUCKING PATIENCE ON YOUR PART, PLEASE?! I'M ABOUT TO BURST INTO FLAME OR START MELTING ANY MINUTE NOW!
THE EXORCIST

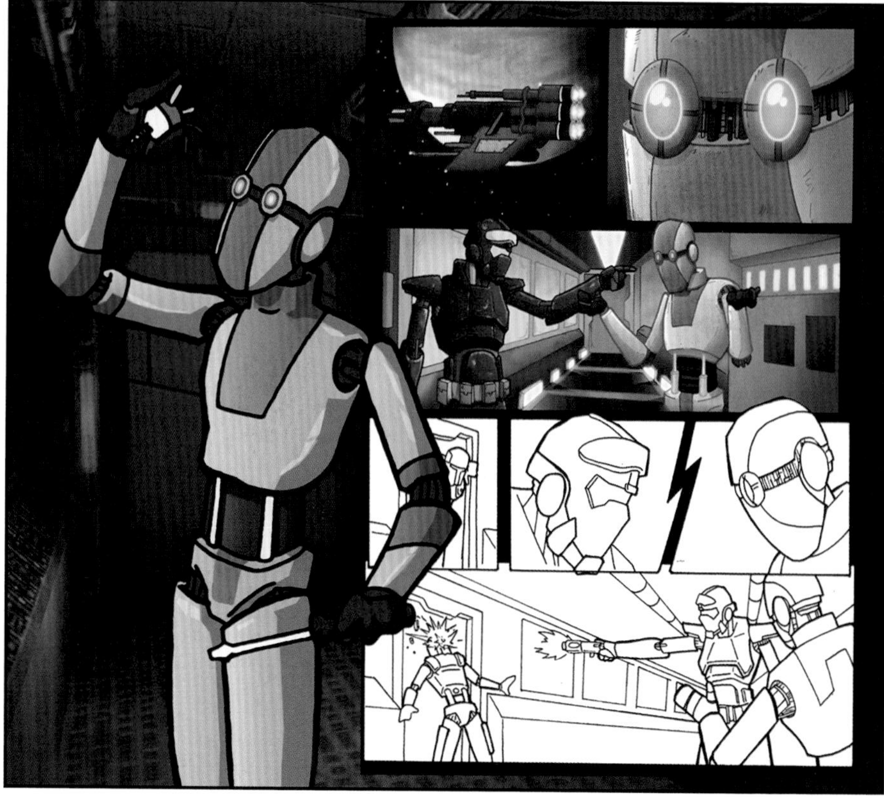

IT MADE ME FEEL PROFESSIONAL. **SO WHAT?** IT WAS JUST A PIECE OF CLOTHING.
ETHAN, THAT STUPID TIE INFECTED YOUR BRAIN.

I **DID** ALMOST LOSE MY **BEST** FRIEND BECAUSE OF THIS WHOLE MESS... I NEVER WOULD HAVE FORGIVEN MYSELF.
I'M SORRY, LUCAS.
IT'S ALRIGHT, ETHAN. DON'T WORRY ABOUT IT.

MAYBE IF I WORE A WHOLE SUIT... OR JUST A NICE PAIR OF SHOES. OOH! WHAT ABOUT A **BOW** TIE?
I AM **NOT** HEARING THIS...

"CUT TO SOME TIME LATER, WHILE I'M IN SUPERMARKET STOCKING ICE CREAM (I WAS WORKING FOR BEN AND JERRY'S AT THE TIME) AND THINKING ABOUT IDEAS FOR CTRL+ALT+DEL STORYLINES. I STARTED THINKING THAT MAYBE IF I COULDN'T DO A STRIP JUST ABOUT ROBOTS, I COULD WRITE ONE INTO CAD. IT'S A GAMING STRIP, SO CREATING A ROBOT OUT OF A VIDEO GAME CONSOLE WAS THE NEXT LOGICAL CONCLUSION. THIS IS HOW THE XBOT IDEA WAS BORN."

HEY ETHAN. WORKING ON STUFF FOR THE VIDEO GAME PROJECT?
SCREW THAT! LOOK! HALO! AND IT'S ON MY PC! INSANITY! HOW COME NO ONE TOLD ME ABOUT THIS?!

GEE, MAYBE BECAUSE YOU WERE LIVING IN YOUR OWN LITTLE WORLD AT THE TIME?
OR PERHAPS IT WAS BECAUSE YOU WERE TOO BUSY DROPPING US ALL LIKE A BAD HABIT FOR A PIECE OF FRUIT?!
OR BOSSING US AROUND BECAUSE OF SOME DAMNED NECKWEAR?!

ETHAN...
WARTHOG GOES FORWARD, WARTHOG GOES BACKWARDS.
WARTHOG TURNS LEFT, WARTHOG RUNS OVER THAT GUY.

WE'LL JUST PUT THE GAME ENGINE ON THE SHELF UNTIL WE'RE READY TO WORK ON IT AGAIN.
BUT AT LEAST WE HAVE THE OLD ETHAN BACK.
I AM ASTONISHED THAT YOU CAN EVEN TELL THE DIFFERENCE.

"I NEVER REALLY LIKED HALO ON THE PC. MAYBE AFTER PLAYING IN THE XBOX EXCLUSIVELY FOR SO LONG, PLAYING IT ON ANY OTHER PLATFORM JUST SEEM UNNATURAL. ALSO, OPENING UP HALO FOR ONLINE PLAY ONLY EXPOSED YOU TO THE MASSES OF RETARDS, WHEREAS BEFORE YOU PLAYED HALO WITH A GROUP OF FRIENDS IN THE SAME ROOM. IT REALLY CHANGED THE WHOLE EXPERIENCE.

I DID LIKE THE DIFFERENT COLORED WARTHOGS THOUGH."

"JAWSOME!"

YOU WANTED TO SEE ME-- OH GOD, YOU HAVE A KNIFE...
HELP ME REMOVE MY JAW.

OK, I KNOW FOR A FACT THAT YOU DID NOT JUST ASK ME TO REMOVE YOUR JAW.
...
YOU DID, DIDN'T YOU? YOU JUST ASKED ME TO REMOVE YOUR JAW...

I SEEM TO HAVE DEVELOPED A NEED TO DEVOUR SOULS.

TO "REAVE" THEM, IF YOU WILL.

RAZIEL TEACHES US THAT IN ORDER TO DO SO, WE MUST BE SANS-JAW.

I SUPPOSE I COULD JUST BUY THE NEW LEGACY OF KAIN IN ORDER TO SATE THIS DESIRE...

DO YOU HAVE FIFTY DOLLARS TO BUY ME A NEW GAME, LUCAS?
GIVE ME THE KNIFE.

"BONUS STRIP!

THIS STRIP WAS MAILED ONLY TO DONATORS IN SEPTEMBER OF 2003. IT WAS NEVER PLACED IN THE CTRL+ALT+DEL ARCHIVES, OR MADE AVAILABLE ONLINE TO THE GENERAL PUBLIC IN ANY WAY AT ALL BEFORE NOW!"

IF *AMERICA'S ARMY* IS ANY INDICATION OF REAL COMBAT...
TONK!

WE KNOW THAT NINE TIMES OUT OF TEN, THE *M203* GRENADE LAUNCHER *NEVER* DETONATES AS IT'S SUPPOSED TO...
?
TONK!

TONK!
...THE HELL?
BUT WITH A LITTLE LUCK...

CRACK!
IT CAN STILL BE A RATHER *EFFECTIVE* WEAPON OF SORTS.

"THIS IS THE LAST *AMERICA'S ARMY* STRIP THAT I DID. THESE COMIC STRIPS WERE ALWAYS A BIG HIT, BUT AS MUCH AS I LOVED THE GAME, I JUST WASN'T PLAYING IT VERY MUCH ANYMORE. IT'S DIFFICULT TO WRITE JOKES ABOUT A GAME YOU'RE NOT PLAYING.

APPARENTLY THE M203 HAS SOME SORT OF RANGE LIMITATION, WHERE IF FIRED AT A TARGET BELOW A 'SAFE' DISTANCE, THE GRENADE WON'T DETONATE. ANNOYING AS HELL IN THE HEAT OF COMBAT."

MUST *HUFF* DANCE! MUST *HUFF HUFF* KEEP PACE!
ALMOST AT THE *PANT* NEXT LEVEL! *WHEEZE*
HELLO. I'M SCOTT, FROM CTRL+ALT+DEL. I'M HERE TODAY TO TALK TO YOU ABOUT A HORRIBLE DISEASE AFFLICTING OUR NATION.
THIS DISEASE IS CALLED DANCE DANCE REVOLUTION, AND IT HAS CONTAMINATED FAR TOO MANY INNOCENT PEOPLE.
PEOPLE WHO HAVE NO BUSINESS DOING ANY SORT OF DANCING IN THE FIRST PLACE.
THESE POOR SOULS SPEND THEIR TIME HAVING ORGANIZED SEIZURES IN FRONT OF SCREENS FULL OF FLASHING LIGHTS, WHILE SPEAKERS BLAST REPETITIVE AND ANNOYING "J-POP".
THESE PEOPLE ARE BEING FOOLED INTO THINKING THEY KNOW HOW TO DANCE. THESE PEOPLE ARE VICTIMS.
BUT THERE IS HOPE. WE CAN SHOW THESE PEOPLE THAT DANCING REQUIRES RHYTHM AND SKILL, NOT JUST FLASHING ARROWS.
CONTACT YOUR LOCAL CHAPTER OF M.A.D.D.R. TO FIND OUT HOW YOU CAN HELP.
PLEASE... THINK OF THE CHILDREN.
M.A.D.D.R.
MANKIND AGAINST DANCE DANCE REVOLUTION

"MY COMICS RARELY SPARK THE IRE OF ENTIRE COMMUNITIES, BUT I FOUND OUT WITH THIS STRIP THAT THE MAJORITY OF DANCE DANCE REVOLUTION PLAYERS ARE OVER-SENSITIVE FREAKS WITH NO SENSE OF HUMOR WHATSOEVER.

MUST HAVE HIT A LITTLE BIT TOO CLOSE TO HOME WITH THIS ONE, EH?"

AHH, SWEET, SWEET SAVAGE. SHALL I TAKE YOU HOME WITH ME?
YES, YES I BELIEVE I SHALL.
AND I'LL LOVE YOU AND FEED YOU AND PLAY WITH YOU A WHOLE FUCKING LOT...

GUH!
FWIP!

HAHA, MISSED ME, SUCKERS!
YOU COULDN'T HIT THE BROAD SIDE OF AN XBOX YOU LOUSY NOOBS!

I REGRET THAT I HAVE BUT ONE LIFE TO WASTE ON VIDEO GAMES!
FWIP!
FWIP!

"THE RANDOM ARROW IS A CLASSIC, BELOVED BY ALMOST ALL CAD FANS. WHILE THE INITIAL JOKE ITSELF IS PRETTY FUNNY, IF YOU'RE GOING TO MAKE SOMETHING LIKE THAT INTO A RECURRING GAG, YOU HAVE TO CONTINUALLY FIND NEW WAYS TO MAKE IT INTERESTING. TO ADD A SURPRISE OR A TWIST TO AN OLD JOKE. IF YOU'RE CAREFUL ABOUT IT, YOU CAN GET SOME DECENT MILEAGE OUT OF A JOKE EVERYONE LOVES. JUST BE MINDFUL OF WHEN THE TIME COMES TO FINALLY RETIRE IT. PREFERABLY BEFORE IT GETS ANNOYING."

"HATE THE CUSTOMER"

CAN I HELP YOU, SIR?
STOP RIGHT THERE, SON. DON'T TRY TO SWINDLE ME. I'VE BEEN USING COMPUTERS SINCE BEFORE YOU WERE BORN. I KNOW ALL THERE IS TO KNOW ABOUT THEM.

OH, THAT'S QUITE OBVIOUS, SIR. AFTER ALL, YOU ARE IN HERE BUYING A PRE-ASSEMBLED P.O.S. RATHER THAN BUILDING YOUR OWN...
YES... YES "P.O.S.", THAT SOUNDS LIKE A GOOD BRAND. TELL ME, HOW MANY JIGGAWATTS DOES THIS UNIT HAVE?

PLANNING ON GOING 'BACK TO THE FUTURE', COMPUTER WHIZ?
WELL, I NEVER!
NEVER TOUCHED A COMPUTER BEFORE? YEAH, I CAN TELL.

"I DID GET ASKED ABOUT THE 'JIGGAWATT' RATING OF A COMPUTER ONCE, WHILE WORKING AT THE BEST BUY STORE IN WARWICK, RHODE ISLAND."

CHEF BRIAN SAYS:
"DEAR CHEF BRIAN, I WAS HOPING YOU COULD TELL ME WHY ELDERLY PEOPLE DRIVE SO SLOW.
YOURS TRULY, BRAD JONES".

FRANKLY BRAD, I DON'T BELIEVE IN THE ELDERLY!
I THINK IT'S A STORY MADE UP TO SCARE LITTLE CHILDREN.
UNLESS, OF COURSE, THE ELDERLY ARE ROBOTS... THAT'S A DIFFERENT STORY.
FOR INSTANCE, IMAGINE THIS EGG HERE WAS AN ELDERLY PERSON...

NOW IMAGINE THAT ALL OF THE GOOEY INSIDE STUFF WAS ROBOTIC PARTS. GEARS AND MICROCHIPS AND THINGS OF THAT NATURE.
SPLUNCH!
REMEMBER... THE EGG IS THE ELDERLY PERSON, AND MY HAND IS SWEET, SWEET JUSTICE.

AND NOW THAT YOU UNDERSTAND, YOU CAN SAVE LIVES!
I RECOMMEND FILLING SOCCER BALLS WITH NAPALM!
NAPALM IS NATURE'S TOOTHPASTE!

"I SWEAR BY MY WACOM GRAPHICS TABLET. I HIGHLY RECOMMEND SOME SORT OF TABLET FOR ANYONE LOOKING TO DO ARTWORK ON THE COMPUTER. I NEVER USE MINE TO DRAW INTO THE COMPUTER FROM SCRATCH (I STILL FIND A PENCIL AND PAPER EASIER AND MORE NATURAL), BUT A TABLET HELPS A LOT WHEN IT COMES TO CLEANING UP LINE ART OR COLORING."

"SPEAK SOFTLY AND..."

SO, WHAT DO YOU SEE HERE? HMM? WHAT DO YOU SEE?

IS IT A FACE? AN ANIMAL? DOES IT MAKE YOU THINK OF SEX?
DO YOU WANT TO KNOW WHAT IT IS? WANT ME TO TELL YOU? I WILL.
IT'S A SPLATTER.
AND IT'S EXACTLY WHAT YOU ARE GOING TO LOOK LIKE IF YOU GET SMACKED BY A BEHEMOTH IN SAVAGE.

BEHEMOTH
YOU
THAT'S NOT A STICK HE'S CARRYING... THAT'S A FUCKING TREE!

AND DO YOU KNOW WHAT THE NAME OF THAT TREE IS? IT HAS A *NAME* YOU KNOW.

ITS NAME IS *"I DON'T FUCKING LIKE YOU, GET OUT OF MY WAY!"*

SAVAGE TIP #35: WHEN A BEHEMOTH SWINGS, BE SOMEWHERE ELSE!

"*SAVAGE* WAS A FPS/RTS GAME THAT I GOT PRETTY HEAVILY HOOKED ON FOR A WHILE. IT WAS TEAM BASED, AND THE TEAM LEADER GOT A TOP-DOWN VIEW LIKE A STRATEGY GAME. HE PLACED BUILDINGS, MANAGED RESOURCES, ETC. BUT THE UNITS WERE ACTUAL PLAYERS, THE REST OF THE TEAM, PLAYING FROM A FPS PERSPECTIVE. THEY WERE IN CHARGE OF ACTUAL COMBAT, MINING RESOURCES AND CONSTRUCTING BUILDINGS.

IT WAS A REALLY GENIUS CONCEPT WITH NEAR PERFECT EXECUTION."

"THE MULTI-TOOL"
ONE OF THE FIRST THINGS YOU'LL NOTICE ABOUT SAVAGE IS THAT NINETY PERCENT OF THE GAME'S ACTIVITIES ARE ACCOMPLISHED WITH JUST ONE MOVE.
I WILL REPAIR THIS BUILDING BY HITTING IT! WITH MY SWORD!
I KILL MY ENEMIES BY HITTING THEM! WITH MY SWORD! REPEATEDLY!
FOR THE LEGION!
MY SWORD HELPS ME MINE RESOURCES, WHICH ALLOWS MY TEAM TO UPGRADE!
MINING INVOLVES HITTING! LOTS OF HITTING!
ALL HAIL TO JARAZIAH!

WITH MY FURIOUS STRIKES I SHALL KNIT THIS SWEATER!
SAVAGE TIP #18: NEED TO GET SOMETHING DONE? BEAT THE CRAP OUT OF IT!

"A REGULAR TRADITION AROUND THE TIME THESE COMICS FIRST CAME OUT WAS SOMETHING I CALLED 'CAD GAMEDAYS'. BASICALLY EVERY WEEKEND I WOULD CHOOSE A GAME (PREFERABLY THE NEWEST FREE MULTIPLAYER DEMO THAT WAS OUT, SO EVERYONE COULD PLAY), AND I WOULD SET A DATE AND TIME THAT I WOULD BE PLAYING. AND FOR A FEW HOURS EVERY WEEKEND, CAD FANS COULD GET TOGETHER WITH OTHER FANS, AND MYSELF, AND PLAY VIDEO GAMES ONLINE FOR A FEW HOURS. I HOPE TO SOMEDAY HAVE THE FREE TIME TO DO SOMETHING LIKE THAT AGAIN."

SAVAGE TIP #67: ALWAYS LISTEN TO YOUR COMMANDER.
GO WASH MY UNDERWEAR WITH WHIPPED CREAM AND A TOOTH-BRUSH.
WHAT. THE. HELL?!
WELL... ALMOST ALWAYS.

SAVAGE TIP #103: DO NOT USE THE BALLISTA TO HUNT CRITTERS! IT IS A WASTE OF RESOURCES!
YEEE-HAAAAW! I GOT ONE!

SAVAGE TIP #22: THE RED FLAG IS NOT A DECORATION! IT MEANS YOU ARE AN OFFICER. ACT LIKE IT!
OOOOH, HOW MAHVELOUS! RED REALLY ISN'T MY COLOR THOUGH... MAKEOVER!

SAVAGE TIP #9: DON'T BE A COWARD! IF YOUR TEAM IS LOSING, DON'T CHANGE SIDES! BE HONORABLE.
HEY... WEREN'T YOU ON OUR TEAM FIVE MINUTES AGO?
UHH... NOPE. DEFINITELY NOT. BEEN A BEAST ALL ALONG. YEP. UHH... GRRRR...

"THE DEVELOPERS OF SAVAGE, *S2GAMES*, WERE BIG FANS OF CTRL+ALT+DEL. WHEN I ANNOUNCED THAT I WANTED TO USE THEIR NEWLY RELEASED DEMO FOR A CAD GAMEDAY, THEY SET US UP OUR OWN OFFICIAL PRIVATE, PASSWORD-PROTECTED SERVER TO PLAY ON. I THINK WE MUST HAVE PLAYED SAVAGE THAT DAY FOR LIKE TWELVE HOURS STRAIGHT, AND WE WERE EVEN JOINED BY SOME S2GAMES STAFF!"

SAVAGE TIP #92: FOR CRYING OUT LOUD, IT'S NOT *EVERQUEST!* DON'T CAMP THE NPC'S! THERE ARE OTHER THINGS THAT DEMAND YOUR ATTENTION!
HOO BOY, AS SOON AS THIS CHIPREL SPAWNS, IT'S GONNA GET IT GOOD.
OH YEAH... *ANY* MINUTE NOW...
AAAANY MINUTE NOW...

"I LOVED SAVAGE, BUT WITH ANY GAME WHERE YOU MIGHT END UP ON A PICK-UP TEAM, IT'S WIN OR LOSE. SOMETIMES YOU GOT ON A SERVER WITH SOME REALLY GREAT PEOPLE, BUT OCCASIONALLY YOU GET GROUPED WITH THE RETARDS WHO ONLY CARE ABOUT THEIR PERSONAL SCORES, AND NOT WHETHER THE TEAM WINS OR LOSES THE MATCH."

HEY, YOU'RE THAT **DETECTIVE** FELLA FROM DOWN THE HALL, **MAX PAYNE,** RIGHT?
I'VE GOT ANOTHER SHOTGUN IF YOU WANT IT. LET ME GET IT FOR YOU.

CAN'T BE TOO CAREFUL THESE DAYS. TOO MANY HOODLUMS AROUND.
WHY, I REMEMBER BACK WHEN I WAS YOUNG... IT WAS A NICE SUMMER DAY...

BLAM!

OH! RIGHT IN THE FACE! ETHAN, **PLEASE** LET ME GET YOU SOME PROFESSIONAL HELP...
WATCH, WATCH. NOW I CAN BLAST HER BODY AROUND THE ROOM WITH THE SHOTGUN.

"RAGDOLL PHYSICS ARE ONE OF THE BEST THINGS TO EVER HAPPEN TO VIDEO GAMES."

"TIME FLIES"

WELL, CTRL+ALT+DEL HAS HIT ITS FIRST YEAR ANNIVERSARY. HOW TIME FLIES, HUH?
WE'VE COME A LOT FARTHER THAN I EVER COULD HAVE IMAGINED POSSIBLE.

EVERYTHING THAT WE HAVE ACCOMPLISHED IS THANKS TO YOU, THE READERS.
WE'D LIKE TO TAKE THIS OPPORTUNITY TO OFFER A VERY HEARTFELT AND SINCERE THANK YOU.

AND I WOULD ALSO LIKE TO--
I BRING THE CAKE! THE CAKE IS IN LEMON FORM!
SSSSSSSSSSSSS

ppy Birthday Ctrl+Alt+
SSSSSSSSSSSSSSS

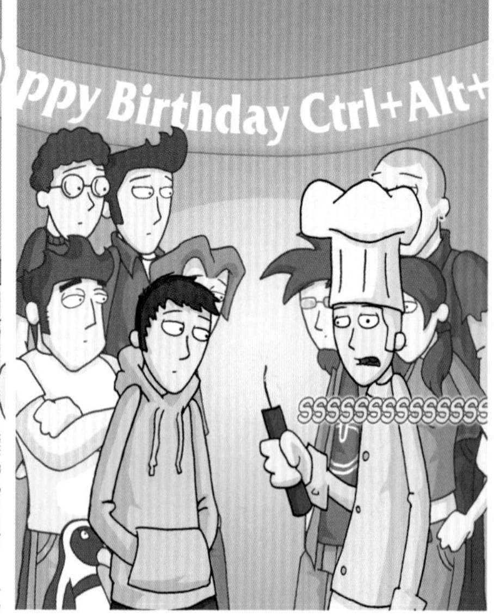

"I AM THE ONLY CHARACTER IN THE COMIC TO REGULARLY CHANGE APPEARANCE OR CLOTHES. THIS IS BECAUSE MY CHARACTER IS OBVIOUSLY BASED OFF OF A REAL PERSON, AND REAL PEOPLE CHANGE OVER TIME. RATHER THAN CREATE A STYLIZED VERSION OF MYSELF THAT WOULD BE APPROPRIATE AT THE TIME, BUT MIGHT NOT ACCURATELY REPRESENT MY APPEARANCE SIX MONTHS OR A YEAR DOWN THE ROAD, EVERY TIME I APPEAR IN THE COMIC I DRAW MYSELF AS I LOOK AT THAT EXACT MOMENT. CLOTHES, HAIR STYLE AND ALL."

HAHAHAHAHA
HAHAHAHAHAHAHAHA
HAHAHAHAHAHA!!

BOOM.
THANK YOU FOR
A WILDLY SUCCESSFUL
FIRST YEAR!

"BELOW YOU CAN SEE THE DESIGN FOR THE VERY
FIRST CTRL+ALT+DEL 'CONSOLE SKIN'. SKINS ARE BASICALLY DECALS
THAT YOU PUT ONTO YOUR VIDEO GAME SYSTEMS
TO FANCY THEM UP A BIT.
THIS ONE WAS FOR THE *GAMEBOY ADVANCE SP* HANDHELD SYSTEM."

TRADE?
PLEASE?

CTRL+ALT+DEL
Tragically L337

PLEASE! ADVENTURERS! YOU *MUST* HELP US!
THE EVIL IS TRYING TO STEAL OUR ***SACRED GOLDEN GLOWING ANKH THINGY!***
THIS ***CAN NOT*** BE ALLOWED TO HAPPEN!

THE ANKH IS VITAL TO THE SURVIVAL OF THE WORLD, FOR UNSPECIFIC REASONS!
IT IS VERY, VERY IMPORTANT!
OH, I CAN TELL THAT YOU DON'T WANT TO LOSE IT.

WHAT, WITH IT LYING OUT ON A PEDESTAL AND ALL.
OPEN. EXPOSED. IN PLAIN VIEW.
AND COMPLETELY UNDEFENDED IN ***ANY*** WAY AT ALL.

WELL, WE ***USED*** TO HAVE A SIGN THAT SAID "PLEASE DO NO STEAL".
I THINK IT GOT STOLEN...

"I DID THIS COMIC AFTER MY TOBY AND I HAD STAYED UP ALL NIGHT PLAYING ***DUNGEONS AND DRAGONS: HEROES*** FOR THE XBOX AND GETTING DRUNK.

AT ABOUT 6AM WE DECIDED TO TAKE A BREAK AND GO UP THE STREET FOR SOME DUNKIN DONUTS. ON THE WAY BACK, TOBY CRASHED HIS CAR HEAD-ON INTO A ROCK WALL.

AFTERWARDS WE WENT HOME AND BEAT THE GAME."

WHOA... YOU SMELL LIKE BOOZE. ARE YOU DRUNK?
I AM A CERTIFIABLE GENIUS!
IT'S ALL IN THE CONTROLLERS! OR THE PLUGS, TO BE MORE EXACT. WE CAN'T PLAY GAMECUBE GAMES ON THE XBOX!
DO YOU KNOW WHY? IT'S BECAUSE YOU CAN'T PLUG THE GAMECUBE CONTROLLER INTO THE XBOX!
THE DESIGNERS ARE TRICKY, SEE? THEY WANT TO KEEP US FROM PLAYING GAMES ON WHATEVER SYSTEM WE WANT!

OH, BUT I FOUND A WAY AROUND THAT. YES, I DID. I FOUND A TOOL THAT LETS ME FIT ANY PLUG INTO THE XBOX.
THE HAMMER... THE HAMMER... YES...
YOU, PLUS ALCOHOL, PLUS A HAMMER... I DON'T IMAGINE OUR XBOX IS IN VERY GOOD SHAPE RIGHT NOW...
NO! YOU CAN'T HAVE IT! IT'S MY DISCOVERY! MY PATENT!

"SO YOU'RE INTERESTED IN STARTING YOUR OWN WEBCOMIC, EH? WELL, IT CAN BE PRETTY TOUGH WORK AT TIMES BUT IT'S ALSO A LOT OF FUN, AND REWARDING IF YOU'RE IN IT FOR THE RIGHT REASONS.

I CAN'T MAKE YOU A SUCCESSFUL WEBCOMIC AUTHOR, BUT I CAN TRY TO OFFER YOU SOME INSIGHT INTO THE MANY THINGS I'VE LEARNED OVER THE YEARS, AND OFFER SOME OF MY OPINIONS AS A PROFESSIONAL IN THE FIELD. SO KEEP AN EYE ON THESE WEBCOMIC ADVICE BOXES FOR SOME HELPFUL TIPS."

"ALL-NIGHTER"

ALRIGHT, EVERYTHING IS LOCKED UP. LET'S CALL IT A NIGHT--
WHAT THE *HELL* ON EARTH?

HUNTER...
THE RECKONING...
REDEEMER!
I *KNOW* YOU HAVE IT IN THERE!

DIBS ON SLEEPING UNDER THE GAMECUBE DISPLAY.
FUCK THAT. I'LL *FIGHT* YOU FOR IT.

"IT'S NO SECRET THAT LUCAS AND I ARE *HUGE* FANS OF GAMES THAT FEATURE COOPERATIVE PLAY. MOST DAYS, WE'D PLAY CO-OP OVER DEATHMATCH IN A SECOND.

HUNTER THE RECKONING SERVED UP A HUGE HELPING OF EXCELLENT CO-OP SHARED-SCREEN MULTIPLAYER. IT'S VERY CHAOTIC, AND REMINISCENT OF THAT GAME *LOADED* FOR THE ORIGINAL PLAYSTATION."

"SOME CHEESE TO GO WITH THAT?"

WHAT IF?
LUKE, I WANT YOU TO GET THESE DROIDS CLEANED UP BEFORE DINNER.
AWWWW, UNCLE OWEN! I WANTED TO GO TO TOSHI STATION AND PICK UP SOME POWER CONVERTERS!

SLAP!

IF YOU WANT TO WHINE LIKE A BITCH, I'M GONNA SLAP YOU LIKE ONE.
YOUR FATHER WAS AN ANNOYING LITTLE BRAT TOO.
I HATE YOU! AND I HATE THE HARVEST! I'M RUNNING AWAY TO JOIN THE EMPIRE!

"MY FAVORITE TRANSFORMER IS *SOUNDWAVE,* OF THE DECEPTICONS."

ETHAN, PLEASE. OUR NEIGHBORS **STILL** GIVE US DIRTY LOOKS AFTER LAST HALLOWEEN.
JUST HAND OUT CANDY AND BE **NICE!**
PFFT. **FINE.**

TRICK OR TREAT, MISTER!
CANDY, CANDY, CANDY, CANDY, CANDY, CANDY, CANDY, CANDY, CANDY...

CANDY, CAND--
SLAM!
THUD!

UHH... IT **FELL...** THE DOOR FELL SHUT.
IT **FELL?!**
IT SLIPPED... UMM... I DIDN'T DO IT?

"THE MOST IMPORTANT BIT OF ADVICE I CAN GIVE YOU CONCERNING THE WORLD OF WEBCOMICS IS THIS, MY CARDINAL LAW:

THERE IS NO ABSOLUTE, INARGUABLE, INCONTROVERTIBLE RIGHT WAY TO DO ANYTHING.

THE ONLY RIGHT WAY IS THE WAY THAT WORKS FOR YOU, AND IT WON'T BE THE SAME FOR ANY TWO PEOPLE. MY ADVICE ISN'T A ROAD MAP TO SUCCESS, ONLY DIRECTIONS TO FINDING THE BEST ROAD FOR YOU."

"MERCY FROM ABOVE"

DO YOU HAVE THE N-GAGE IN STOCK? I'D LIKE TO PURCHASE ONE.
WHAT DID YOU JUST SAY TO ME?
N-GAGE? I'D LIKE TO BUY ONE.
ARE YOU TRYING TO BE FUNNY?
UHH... NO?

YEAH... OK. WE'VE GOT ONE. IT'S ON THE SHELF... IN STORAGE. LET ME JUST GET THE LADDER. YOU STAND RIGHT THERE.
I'M GLAD YOU GUYS HAVE ONE. NO OTHER STORE SELLS THEM.

CRACK!
I THINK THE CONCEPT OF A CELL PHONE GAMING SYSTEM IS GREA-
AGH!

GAH! UNCONSCIOUS BODY ON THE SALES FLOOR! ETHAN! WHAT HAPPENED?!
GEE, I'M NOT TOO SURE, BARRY...
IF I HAD TO VENTURE A GUESS, I'D SAY HE PASSED OUT FROM AN OVERDOSE OF RETARDISM.

"WHY STOP AT JUST COMBINING A CELL PHONE AND HAND-HELD VIDEO GAME SYSTEM? IF WE'RE GOING TO START PUTTING OUT HALF-ASSED HYBRIDS, LET'S GO ALL THE WAY.

HOW ABOUT A CELL PHONE THAT IS ALSO A TOASTER? YOU COULD HAVE TOAST ANY TIME YOU WANTED. OOH, OR A CELL PHONE THAT IS ALSO A RAKE. I CAN'T TELL YOU HOW MANY TIMES I'VE WANTED TO TALK ON THE PHONE WHILE RAKING LEAVES..."

"FLYING SOLO"

HEY BUDDY, UP FOR A BIT OF LAN MAYHEM TONIGHT?
NO CAN DO, ETHAN. WE'RE DOING INVENTORY AT THE STORE. I'VE GOT TO WORK ALL NIGHT.

SO, LILAH, HOW ABOUT I MAKE YOU DINNER TONIGHT?
I'M THINKING SOME PIZZA DELIVERY, FOLLOWED BY RELAXING IN FRONT OF THE WARM GLOW OF THE TV...
GOING TO THE "GYM"? NEVER HEARD OF IT... THAT THE NAME OF THE NEW ARCADE IN THE MALL?

UH... SCOTT?
CAN NOT CONVERSATE RIGHT NOW, ETHAN. I'M TRYING TO EXPAND MY COSMIC CONSCIOUSNESS.
YOU CAN JOIN ME, IF YOU'D LIKE.
UM, YEAH... PASS ON THAT.

SO, UHH... TED. WHAT'S UP?
YEAH... SO...
OH SHIT... THIS IS WHAT ROCK-BOTTOM FEELS LIKE, ISN'T IT?

"IN MY OPINION, STARTING A WEBCOMIC FOR THE PURPOSE OF MAKING MONEY IS THE WRONG REASON TO START A WEBCOMIC. THE PERCENTAGE OF PEOPLE MAKING A LIVING AT IT IS EXTREMELY SMALL WHEN COMPARED TO THE SHEER NUMBER OF WEBCOMICS ONLINE. IF YOU THINK A WEBCOMIC WILL MAKE YOU RICH AND FAMOUS, YOU'RE SETTING YOURSELF UP FOR DISAPPOINTMENT. HOWEVER IF YOU'RE INTERESTED IN STARTING A WEBCOMIC BECAUSE YOU REALLY WANT TO EXPRESS YOUR CREATIVE VISION, THERE IS NO WAY YOU CAN COME TO FAILURE."

NOBODY HAS ANY TIME FOR *ME*, HUH?
EVERYONE IS *TOO BUSY* TO HANG OUT WITH ME, IS THAT HOW IT IS?

WHO NEEDS THEM, ANYWAY?
NOT ME, THAT'S FOR DAMNED SURE.
I'M RESOURCEFUL. I'M CREATIVE. I'M *TOTALLY* AND COMPLETELY SANE.

THEY'LL ALL COME CRAWLING BACK WHEN I'M DONE.
OH YES THEY WILL...
"BZZT" INDEED, *MR. BATTERY.*
BZZZZT
BZZZZT

I AM THE MASTER OF MY OWN DESTINY.
I SHALL BE A *GOD* IN MY OWN RIGHT.
FFSSHHH
I THINK I JUST SET MY *PANTS* ON FIRE... *BUT IT MATTERS NOT!*

"THERE ARE CERTAIN GENRES IN THE WEBCOMICS FIELD THAT ARE PERCEIVED AS A BIT OVER-SATURATED. THE 'GAMING WEBCOMIC' GENRE IS ONE OF THEM. ALSO INCLUDED ARE THE 'COLLEGE' AND 'REAL LIFE' GENRES.

THE BOTTOM LINE, HOWEVER, IS THAT IT'S *YOUR* COMIC. CREATE YOUR COMIC TO MAKE *YOU* HAPPY, AND DON'T WORRY ABOUT ANYONE ELSE. YOU ARE THE ONLY PERSON WHOSE STANDARDS YOU NEED TO MEET ONE-HUNDRED PERCENT OF THE TIME."

"COMMENCE EVACUATION

HEY SCOTT, HAVE YOU SEEN THE XBOX? I CAN'T FIND IT ANYWHERE.
NO, I HAVEN'T. SORRY.
BY THE WAY, ETHAN HAS BEEN IN HIS ROOM ALL DAY TALKING TO HIMSELF.

BBBZZZRT!!
BBZZZZWOOOOOO
SO UHH... I THINK I'M GOING TO GO FOR A DRIVE...
YEAH? WHERE ARE YOU HEADED?
FAR, FAR AWAY. WANT TO COME?
THOUGHT YOU'D NEVER ASK.

CLUNK!
ZZZZMMMMMMMMMM
I NEED MORE POWER!!
DEAR GOD! MY PANTS ARE ON FIRE AGAIN!!

"ONE OF THE PHILOSOPHIES THAT I TRY TO INCORPORATE INTO MY WORK ETHIC, AND DAY-TO-DAY LIFE IS SOMETHING THAT BRUCE LEE ONCE SAID:

'KNOWING IS NOT ENOUGH, WE MUST APPLY. WILLING IS NOT ENOUGH, WE MUST DO.'"

"CHERRY FLAVORED"

UNGH, GET IN THERE, DAMNIT!
OH, SO THAT'S WHERE THAT GOES!
OH, YOU ARE A SEXY BEAST, AREN'T YOU?
WHERE'S MY SCREW-DRIVER?
HRMM... TOO BIG...
KEEP OUT!
WHATAREYOU DOINGOUTSIDEOF MYDOORSNOOPING AROUNDWHODOYOUWORK FORWHATDOYOUWANT AREYOUTRYINGTO STEALMYWORK?!
SLAM!
ETHAN, WHAT ARE YOU DOING IN THERE ALL DAY? I'M WORRIED ABOUT YOU.
EWW! IS THAT BLOOD?
WHAT? OH... NO, IT'S KOOL-AID. THE COVER POPPED OFF MY SIPPY CUP.
NOTHING.
WHAT?!

"CLASSIC FRANKENSTEIN POSTER IN THE BACKGROUND THERE, SORT OF DROPPING A HINT AT THE TIME FOR THE MORE PERCEPTIVE READERS, AND FORESHADOWING THE THINGS TO COME."

"SPILLED MILK

GRUMBLE TOO EARLY... *MUMBLE MUMBLE* G'MORNING...
MEH.
HI.

DID YOU KNOW THAT WE'RE OUT OF **CEREAL?** WHAT AM I SUPPOSED TO PUT INTO MY **MILK?**

CRASH!

YOU'D **BETTER** BE PLANNING ON CLEANING THAT UP, HUMAN.

"I TRIED OUT NUMEROUS DIFFERENT DESIGNS FOR THE XBOT, BUT WAS HAVING TROUBLE SETTLING ON ONE THAT I WAS HAPPY WITH. IN THE END I DECIDED TO REVISIT AN EARLIER CHARACTER CONCEPT FROM A DIFFERENT PROJECT THAT HAD NEVER GOTTEN OFF THE GROUND.

WITH A LITTLE TWEAKING AND A NEW COLOR PALATE, IT BECAME THE XBOT WE ALL KNOW AND LOVE TODAY."

ETHAN... WHAT THE... HOW DID... WHEN... WHAT... WHAT DID YOU DO?!
YOU'RE NOT ALLOWED TO BE UPSET, "MR. DITCH-YOUR-FRIENDS-FOR WORK".

WELL, HAD I KNOWN THAT YOU WERE GOING TO HAVE A PSYCHOTIC EPISODE AND RUIN OUR XBOX, I WOULD HAVE CALLED IN SICK.
NOT RUINED. IMPROVED.

OH YEAH? WHAT DOES IT DO? VACUUM? DO THE LAUNDRY?
AS WELL AS PLAYING IMPORTS!

AND I CAN PLAY WITH MYSELF.
SNICKER
OH FOR CRYING OUT LOUD! AS IF ONE WASN'T BAD ENOUGH!

"WHEN IT COMES TO WRITING AND ART, YOUR ONLY BOUNDARIES ARE THOSE SET BY YOUR OWN IMAGINATION. YOU CAN DO WHATEVER YOU WANT, IN WHATEVER WAY YOU WANT. I ALWAYS TRY TO KEEP MOST OF MY COMIC GROUNDED IN REALITY, IN EVERY DAY STUFF, SO THAT WHEN I DO CRAZY THINGS, SUCH AS INTRODUCE A SENTIENT CONSOLE ROBOT, THEY SEEM MUCH MORE BELIEVABLE."

SO DOES IT HAVE A NAME? WHAT ARE WE GOING TO CALL IT?
OBVIOUSLY WE SHALL CALL HIM 'ETHAN 2'. OR PERHAPS 'ETHAN JUNIOR'.
OBVIOUSLY THAT IS THE STUPIDEST IDEA EVER.

WE'LL CALL HIM RUPERT. AS A TRIBUTE.
JACOB?
CORNELIUS.
TOBIAS.
CHADWICK?
NO.

HOURS LATER...
HMM... LAST ONE ON THE LIST. UMM... ZAPNUT?
FINE. YOU KNOW WHAT? I DON'T EVEN CARE WHAT WE CALL IT ANYMORE.
HEY, FROM NOW ON YOUR NAME IS ZAPNUT.
CLEARLY YOUR FRAIL HUMAN BRAIN IS SUFFERING SOME SORT OF MALFUNCTION.
UGH. WHATEVER. YOU DON'T GET A NAME, THEN. WE'LL JUST CALL YOU "HEY SHITHEAD".

"THIS COMIC WAS REFLECTIVE OF THE TROUBLE THAT I WAS HAVING COMING UP WITH A NAME FOR THE XBOT. HE WAS GOING TO HAVE THE NAME FOR THE REST OF HIS LIFE, AND HE'S A WALKING, TALKING SENTIENT CONSOLE ROBOT. YOU CAN'T JUST GIVE HIM A REGULAR NAME LIKE 'JOE'.

IN THE END I DECIDED TO JUST TRY OUT CALLING HIM 'THE XBOT FOR A WHILE. IT WOULDN'T BE UNTIL MONTHS AND MONTHS LATER THAT HE WOULD FINALLY RECEIVE HIS REAL NAME."

"COMPROMISES"

SO, UHH... YEAH. I KIND OF WANTED TO PLAY SOME RAINBOW SIX 3... SO...

MEH. I'M NOT IN THE MOOD FOR THAT RIGHT NOW. LET'S PLAY SOME GRAND THEFT AUTO!

HEY, LISTEN UP, YOU SCRAP-HEAP. IF IT WAS UP TO ME YOU'D STILL BE INANIMATE. I DON'T FEEL I SHOULD HAVE TO WORRY ABOUT WHAT MY CONSOLES ARE IN THE MOOD FOR.
BUT GIVEN THE SITUATION WE'RE GOING TO HAVE TO WORK ON SOME COMPROMISES HERE.

FINE.
VVVV-CLICK!

THAT'S WHERE HE PUT THE CD TRAY?
YES'M.
URGE TO GAME... FADING...
OH, SURE, NOW THAT YOU'VE GOT ME ALL WORKED UP.

"I'VE FOUND THAT HUMANS AREN'T PARTICULARLY EASY TO UPGRADE. YOUR HARDWARE IS VERY FLIMSY, AND CREATES SUCH A MESS.

AND YOUR FIRMWARE IS NIGH IMPOSSIBLE TO UPDATE."

I SWEAR THAT HELL MUST HAVE FROZEN OVER. IS THAT AN IPOD? YOU PURCHASED AN APPLE PRODUCT?
GAH! NO! NEVER! I DID NOTHING! NOTHING!
WHAT IS THAT IN YOUR HAND THEN?
THIS? OH... THIS IS... A POP-TART
WHAT FLAVOR?
CINNAMON AND SUGAR.
PROVE IT.
GOOD MORNING ETHAN, THE NURSE HAS TOLD ME THAT YOU'RE HAVING A PROBLEM WITH-- OH SWEET GOD AND ALL THAT IS HOLY!
UCK OO, UTHER UCKER.

"YOUR UPDATE SCHEDULE IS A VITAL PART OF YOUR COMIC. THIS SCHEDULE LETS PEOPLE KNOW WHEN TO CHECK YOUR WEBSITE FOR A NEW COMIC. IF YOU WANT TO DEVELOP A GOOD RELATIONSHIP WITH YOUR AUDIENCE, THEY NEED TO BE ABLE TO COUNT ON A NEW COMIC WHEN YOU SAY IT WILL BE UP.

BECAUSE OF THIS, MAKE SURE YOU CHOOSE AN UPDATE SCHEDULE YOU CAN MAINTAIN, AND DON'T BE AFRAID TO ALTER IT IF IT BECOMES TOO MUCH FOR YOU TO HANDLE."

A LITTLE ROMANCE...

A LITTLE ATMOSPHERE...

A LITTLE "GETTIN' BUSY" MUSIC...
LOADING CD...
SOME TIMES YOU NEED LOVIN' MORNING, NOON AND NIGHT, MAKES NO DIFFERENCE WHEN IT IS, MY DARLING, IT'S ALRIGHT!

BABY, YOU AND I WERE MADE FOR EACHOTHER.
I WANT YOU *IN* ME.

"THAT'S A LITTLE BIT OF ***BARRY WHITE,*** FOR YOU UNEDUCATED MAMMALS. GUARANTEED TO PUT ANY LADY IN THE MOOD.

ABOUT ONE OF THE ONLY WORTHWHILE CONTRIBUTIONS YOUR KIND HAS MADE TO THIS EXISTENCE. WELL, APART FROM YOUR ROBOTIC BRETHREN, THAT IS."

"NO BANDWIDTH FOR YOU!"

GAY MARRIAGE? GROOVY. IT'S ABOUT TIME. WAY TO GO ***MASSACHUSETTS.*** MORE POWER TO--
HEY, WHAT THE... "CONNECTION LOST"? THAT'S STRANGE.

MAYBE THE NETWORK CABLE GOT UNPLUGGED SOMEWHERE...
PIRATES

SLURP MMM... *GULP*

MMM! *SLURP* BANDWIDTH ***GOOOOD.*** *SLURP* XBOX LIVE. WANT SOME? MMM TASTY.

"MASSACHUSETTS TOOK A HUGE STEP FORWARD FOR HUMAN RIGHTS AND LEGALIZED GAY MARRIAGE.

PRETTY GROOVY, HUH?

IT'S ALL ABOUT FREEDOM FROM OPPRESSION, MAN.

NEXT UP, FREEDOM FROM THE TYRANNY OF MICROSOFT."

ETHAN, HAVE YOU EVEN CONSIDERED THE ETHICAL AND MORAL IMPLICATIONS HERE?!
YOU... YOU CAN'T JUST... CREATE LIFE!

YOU HAVE TO BE CONCERNED WITH--
HEY, CAN ONE OF YOU MEATBAGS GIVE ME A HAND? I'M TRYING TO INSTALL A LINUX DASHBOARD OVER MY DEFAULT SOFTWARE.

HEY, DINNER AND A MOVIE FIRST, PAL. DINNER AND A MOVIE.
YOU TRAITOROUS BASTARD...

"YOU MEATSACKS ARE TOO SOFT. I'M AFRAID THAT IF I LOOK AT YOU WRONG I'LL PUNCTURE THAT THIN, FLESHY SHELL THAT HOLDS ALL OF YOUR SMOOSHY-BITS IN CHECK."

I'VE BEEN PRETTY GOOD ABOUT IT, FOR THE **MOST** PART.
AND I TRY TO IGNORE IT WHEN IT COMES TO MIND.
BUT SOMETIMES I FEEL LIKE THERE IS JUST **NO** ESCAPING IT.
IT HAUNTS ME. IT HAUNTS MY **DREAMS.**

I'VE TRIED TO FILL THE VOID. I'VE TRIED EVERY SUBSTITUTE AVAILABLE.
ANARCHY ONLINE, ASHERON'S CALL, DARK AGE OF CAMELOT...
NONE OF THEM BAIT ME LIKE SHE DID.
NONE OF THEM **LOVE** ME LIKE SHE DID...

I FEAR THAT IT'S ONLY A MATTER OF TIME BEFORE SHE SUCKS ME BACK IN.
I HAVEN'T FORGOTTEN WHAT SHE DID TO ME... BUT I FEEL COMPELLED TO **FORGIVE...**
I DON'T KNOW HOW MUCH LONGER I CAN HOLD OUT...

IT'S IN MY **BLOOD!** LIKE SOME SORT OF DRUG ADDICTION THAT WON'T LET GO! **EVERQUEST!** I LONG FOR HER SWEET, SWEET EMBRACE!
I CAN NOT IGNORE HER CALL! I FIEND! **I FIEND!**
PLEASE DON'T HURT ME!

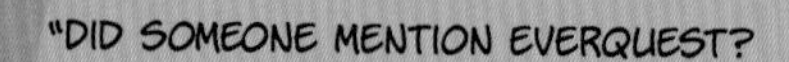

"DID SOMEONE MENTION EVERQUEST?

YOU KNOW... I HAVEN'T PLAYED THAT GAME IN A LONG TIME. I'M A LOT BETTER NOW. I COULD PROBABLY HANDLE IT.

...

I'VE GOTTA RUN TO THE STORE FOR A SECOND..."

HEY ETHAN. IN ON YOUR DAY OFF?
GAMES! RING THEM UP! CHARGE IT! CHARGE IT NOW!

FINAL FANTASY XI, SHADOWBANE, PHANTASY STAR ONLINE...
QUICKLY NOW! THERE ISN'T MUCH TIME! I FEEL HER ICY COLD FINGERS ALONG MY SPINE!
ETHAN, CALL ME CRAZY, BUT THIS DOESN'T SEEM LIKE A GOOD IDEA TO ME...

ACK! TOO LATE! MY LEGS ARE GOING NUMB! I'M SUCCUMBING! WE MUST ACT FAST!
HURRY! GRIND UP ONE OF THOSE GAME DISCS INTO A FINE POWDER! I'LL JUST SNORT IT! AUGH! WHAT ARE YOU WAITING FOR?!

HEY ROB... I THINK I'M GOING TO NEED YOU TO PICK UP SOME EXTRA SHIFTS THIS WEEK...
DUDE, OK GUY! THAT REMINDS ME OF THIS TIME IN COUNTER-
YEAH, OK, GOOD. SHUT UP NOW.
OH GOD... THE SHAKES... THE SHAKES...

"ONE OF THE PERKS OF MY JOB IS THAT IT OFTEN SCORES ME SOME PRETTY NIFTY STUFF, LIKE REVIEW COPIES OF GAMES, AND SPOTS IN CLOSED BETA TESTS.

IT'S A DIRTY JOB, BUT SOMEONE HAS TO DO IT."

"SWIMMING IN WHAT?!"

AHH. WELL, THIS IS AN INTERESTING SENSATION...
ALMOST LIKE... SWIMMING. IN JELL-O.
HEHE. JELL-O.

Ethan
OH. SOLID GROUND. THAT'S NICE TOO... I GUESS.
I'M STILL IN ONE PIECE... NOT MISSING ANY LIMBS... I DON'T FEEL DEAD...
OH, WAIT... WHEN DID THAT GET THERE?

Ethan
A Giant Rat

Ethan
YO.
AUGH!
A Giant Rat

"FOR ANYONE WHO EVER PLAYED EVERQUEST, THE 'A GIANT RAT' WILL ALWAYS HOLD A SPECIAL PLACE IN THEIR HEART.

SCOURGE OF THE NEWBIE LANDS, DROPPED OF THE MYSTERIOUS RUSTY SHORT SWORDS AND CLOTH BRACERS, TWITCHY EYEBALLS OF DOOOOOOM."

"GOING HOME"

QUICK! YOU'VE GOT TO HELP ME! I DON'T KNOW HOW I GOT HERE, BUT I DON'T BELONG!
I NEED TO GO HOME! NOW!

HEY! BUCKET HEAD! DON'T JUST STAND THERE!
HELP ME!

YOU'VE RUINED YOUR OWN LANDS, YOU'LL NOT RUIN MINE!
WHAM!
WHAM!
WHAM!
WHAM!
WHAM!
WHAM!

Guard Jacen
OW, OW, OW, OW, OW, OW, OW... OW.
FUCKING OW!
LOADING... PLEASE WAIT...
Ethan's Corpse

"NEVER, EVER, EVER LAY A HAND ON THE FREEPORT GUARDS. DON'T EVEN LOOK AT THEM FUNNY. IN FACT, DON'T EVEN FUCKING THINK ABOUT THEM. THEY WILL FLATTEN YOU IN A HEARTBEAT.

THE FIRST TIME I MADE THE TRIP FROM HALAS TO FREEPORT, I FINALLY GOT THE GATES, AND DECIDED TO HAIL THE GUARDS. BUT I HIT THE WRONG BUTTON AND ATTACKED THEM. AND NO APOLOGY WAS GOING TO CUT IT. AN HOUR OF TRAVEL AND I WAS BACK IN HALAS IN FIVE MINUTES."

MUAHAH! DING, I SAY! DING! LEVEL UP! CONGRATS TO ME! I AM A GOD!
ETHAN. HEY, ETHAN. HEY BUDDY. HEY, ETHAN...

ETHAN... HEY... ETHAN...
AUGH! TRAIN TO ZONE! TRAIN TO ZONE!
HEY, IT'S ALRIGHT. RELAX. YOU WERE ASLEEP. YOU PASSED OUT AT WORK.

WANT TO... NO... HAVE TO... PLAY EVERQUEST. MUST... GIVE IN...
EVERQUEST KEEPS ME SANE...
EVERQUEST?

NURSE! WE'RE GOING TO NEED SOME SEDATIVES IN HERE!
LIKE, HORSE TRANQUILIZERS IF YOU HAVE ANY!
OUT OF MANA... MUST MEDITATE... MUST... CAMP THE SPAWN...

"THE TERM **MMORPG** STANDS FOR 'MASSIVELY MULTIPLAYER ONLINE GAME', OR 'GIVE UP THE IDEA OF EVER HAVING A LIFE, BECAUSE YOU BELONG TO THE GAME NOW, SUCKER'.

BASICALLY IT'S AN RPG THAT IS ONLY PLAYED ONLINE, WHERE YOU CREATE A CHARACTER IN A PERSISTENT WORLD WITH THOUSANDS OF OTHER PLAYERS FROM AROUND THE WORLD, AND SINK HOUR AFTER HOUR OF YOUR VALUABLE TIME INTO MENIAL, REPETITIVE TASKS. AND YOU LOVE EVERY FUCKING MINUTE OF IT AND ASK FOR MORE."

"DESPERATION SETS IN..."

HEY MAN, YOU'VE BEATEN THIS BEFORE, YOU CAN BEAT IT AGAIN.
YOU JUST HAD A LITTLE SLIP, THAT'S ALL.

HEY, LILAH HAS BEEN ASKING ABOUT YOU. SHE'S CONCERNED ABOUT YOU.
EVEN SCOTT AND THAT STUPID XBOT HAVE BEEN WORRIED.
I'M NOT SURE IF I CAN FACE THEM RIGHT NOW...

I FEEL LIKE I LET EVERYONE DOWN. I ALMOST GAVE IN TO THE URGES...
DON'T WORRY ABOUT IT. I'LL GO HOOK UP THE LAN. WE'LL GET YOUR MIND OFF OF IT.

HEY... I WAS THINKING... MAYBE I SHOULDN'T DO THIS COLD TURKEY...
MAYBE JUST ONE TEENSY LITTLE EVERQUEST ACCOUNT?
I'D EVEN PLAY A RANGER!
OR... OR IF NOT, I'D EVEN SETTLE FOR SOME LORDS OF EVERQUEST!
PLEASE?!

"TWO OF MY BIGGEST INTERESTS ARE VIDEO GAMES AND DRAWING (GO FIGURE) BUT MY OTHER INTERESTS INCLUDE EXERCISE, CARS, FILM, READING, WRITING, PAINTBALL AND MORE."

SIGH IT HAS BEEN A WHILE SINCE I'VE ATTENDED ONE OF THESE...
HELLO EVERYONE... MY NAME IS ETHAN... AND I AM A RECOVERING EVERQUEST ADDICT.
E.A.U
Everquest Addicts United
Letting go together.
HI ETHAN.
HELLO ETHAN.
HI ETHAN.
WELCOME ETHAN.
I'VE BEEN CLEAN FOR TWO YEARS... I THOUGHT I HAD BEATEN IT.
BUT JUST RECENTLY I ALMOST SUFFERED A RELAPSE...
THANKFULLY, I DIDN'T MANAGE TO GET MY HANDS ON AN EVERQUEST ACCOUNT...
I'M FOLLOWING THE STEPS IN THE HANDBOOK... TRYING TO DISTRACT MYSELF WITH OTHER MMORPG'S...

AMEN, BROTHER! WE KNOW HOW YOU FEEL!
SOMETIMES I DRESS IN TIGHTS OR A SKIMPY BIKINI BECAUSE I DESPERATELY WANT TO BE A WOOD ELF FEMALE!

OK... YEAH DUDE, THAT'S PRETTY FUCKED UP RIGHT THERE...
LIKE SERIOUSLY MESSED UP. YOU NEED SOME HELP.
NO GROUP HUG FOR YOU LATER... I MEAN THAT.
SIT THE FUCK DOWN.

"ETHAN IS FINE WHEN HE IS PLAYING *ANY* OTHER MMORPG. DARK AGE OF CAMELOT, STAR WARS GALAXIES, ASHERON'S CALL, WHATEVER.

THERE'S JUST SOMETHING ABOUT EVERQUEST THAT POISONS HIS MIND. NORRATH DOES TO ETHAN WHAT FIRE DOES TO GASOLINE. IT'S NOT PRETTY."

"VICIOUS CYCLE"

WELL, LET'S SEE IF *FINAL FANTASY XI* CAN DISTRACT ME... AT LEAST FOR A LITTLE WHILE.

THREE HOURS LATER...
PFFT! EVERQUEST, EAT YOUR HEART OUT. THIS GAME ROCKS MY PROVERBIAL SOCKS. SO LONG *EQ!* ADDICTION STATUS: *CURED!*

TEN HOURS LATER...
BRAIN... SHUTTING DOWN. MUST... KEEP PLAYING. JUST A LITTLE WHILE LONGER...
JUST UNTIL I CATCH UP TO THE JAPANESE PLAYERS... YEAH... THAT SOUNDS LIKE A RATIONAL EXCUSE...

THIRTY-SIX HOURS LATER...
GEEZ, THIS GAME IS AWESOME. I CAN'T STOP PLAYING!
IT'S ALMOST LIKE AN ADDICTIO-- *FUCK!*

"IF YOU ARE A WRITER WITH LITTLE OR NO ARTISTIC SKILLS, I HIGHLY RECOMMEND TRYING TO FIND YOURSELF AN ARTIST TO TEAM UP WITH. SPRITE COMICS ARE ONE SOLUTION, BUT THEY HAVE A VERY, VERY BAD STIGMA SURROUNDING THEM, WHICH COULD MAKE THE INITIAL REACTION TO YOUR COMIC LESS THAN FAVORABLE.

MANY PEOPLE WON'T EVEN BOTHER TO SEE WHAT YOUR STORY IS ABOUT, IF THEY GET TURNED OFF BY THE POOR REPUTATION OF SPRITE COMICS."

HEY, DO YOU WANT TO GROUP UP FOR SOME-- OH MY GOD, WHAT THE HELL IS THAT THING?! HAHAHAHA!
DON'T EVEN START. I MEAN IT.
SO, UHH... HOW'S THE WEATHER UP THERE?
SHUT UP.
MUST BE A PAIN TO SHOP FOR TURTLE-NECKS THAT FIT.
FUCK YOU.
YOU COULD FLY A FLAG FROM THAT THING!
YOU KNOW WHAT? NO HEALS FOR YOU NOW.
HEY... UP FOR SOME TETHER-BALL?
YEAH, YOU'RE DEFINITELY DYING A MOST PAINFUL DEATH WHILE I STAND BY AND WATCH.
SURE THING, STRETCH!
ASS.
FINAL FANTASY XI: THE ONLY RPG TO CROSS-BREED ELVES WITH GIRAFFES.

"I ACTUALLY STARTED PLAYING FINAL FANTASY XI AT THE INSISTENCE OF PONTUS MADSEN OF LITTLE GAMERS. I THOUGH THE GRAPHICS WERE PRETTY GOOD, BUT I DIDN'T STICK WITH IT VERY LONG. I'VE NEVER BEEN A HUGE FAN OF THE FINAL FANTASY SERIES, SO PERHAPS THAT'S WHY I COULDN'T GET INTO IT.

PLUS I HAD A HARD TIME GETTING PAST THE SILLY RACES IN THE GAME. ESPECIALLY THOSE STUPID LOOKING ELVES."

"PEARLY WHITES"

CREST WHITE STRIPS... "DO NOT SWALLOW STRIPS. DO NOT GET GEL MATERIAL IN EYES"...
...

THAT HAS GOT TO BE THE ABSOLUTE MOST RETARDED WARNING LABEL I HAVE EVER SEEN.

STICK

AUUUGH! FOR THE LOVE OF ALL THAT IS HOLY! HOW THE HELL DID I MANAGE TO MISS MY TEETH ALTOGETHER?! OH THE IRONY! THE BURNS!
AUGH!!
GOING TO CALL 911?
I CALLED THEM BEFORE HE EVEN OPENED THE BOX.

"THAT WARNING LABEL WAS REALLY ON THE BOX. CERTAIN THINGS YOU JUST ASSUME ARE COMMON SENSE, BUT YOU'D BE SURPRISED...

LUCAS IS READING 'A STORM OF SWORDS', THE THIRD BOOK IN MY FAVORITE FANTASY SERIES OF ALL TIME, ***A SONG OF ICE AND FIRE*** BY GEORGE R. R. MARTIN. IF YOU'RE NOT FAMILIAR WITH IT, I HIGHLY RECOMMEND GOING OUT AND BUYING THE FIRST BOOK, 'A GAME OF THRONES'. AFTER YOU FINISH THIS BOOK, OF COURSE."

I'M IN LOS ANGELES COMPETING TO BE THE WORLD'S SEXIEST GAMER!

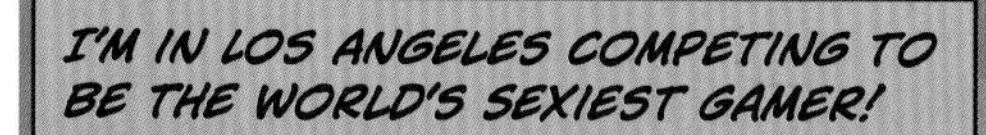

SO TELL US, IF YOU WERE TO WIN THE **WORLD'S SEXIEST GAMER COMPETITION,** WHAT WOULD YOU DO?

WHAT WOULD I DO? I'LL TELL YOU WHAT I'D DO! NONE OF THAT "WORLD PEACE" AND "END HUNGER" CRAP, THAT'S FOR SURE!

I'D MAKE SURE THAT EVERY PERSON ON THE PLANET HAD AN **XBOX** AND A COPY OF **HALO.**

THEN WE'D **LAN** SO HARD THAT YOU WOULD BE ABLE TO SEE MASTER CHIEF FROM FUCKING **SPACE!**

AND I'D REFORM **BLACK ISLE STUDIOS** AND MAKE THEM FINISH **FALLOUT 3,** BECAUSE WE DESERVE THAT GAME, DAMNIT!

AND... AND... I'D HAVE THE WORLD'S LARGEST COMPUTER MADE... OUT OF **CAKE!!**

OH, AND I HAVE A WHOLE **LIST** OF PEOPLE I'D LIKE TO KICK IN THE NUTS!

WISH ME LUCK!

"IN THE WINTER OF 2003 I WAS A FINALIST IN A COMPETITION BEING RUN BY A GAMING WEBSITE CALLED 'THE WORLD'S SEXIEST GAMER'. AFTER THREE MONTHS OF ONLINE VOTING AND SEMI-FINALS, TEN FINALISTS (FIVE GUYS AND FIVE GIRLS) WERE FLOWN OUT TO LOS ANGELES TO COMPETE LIVE AT UNIVERSAL STUDIOS. THERE WAS GAMING TRIVIA, A SOUL CALIBUR 2 TOURNAMENT AND A 'SEXY DANCE' COMPETITION. I DIDN'T END UP WINNING, BUT IT WAS A FUN AND FREE TRIP TO CALIFORNIA. IT WAS ALSO TELEVISED ON *TECHTV.*"

"MUCH DESERVED"

X-BOX

HEY, I COULDN'T HELP BUT NOTICE YOU LOOKING AT A COPY OF DEUS EX 2...
OH NO. DON'T EVEN SAY IT. I'M NOT IN THE MOOD.
DEUS EX ISN'T REALLY MADE FOR GIRLS. PERHAPS WE COULD FIND YOU A MY LITTLE PONY GAME. HEHE.

SNICKER

YEAH, WELL YOUR FACE ISN'T REALLY MADE FOR GIRLS EITHER.
MAYBE WE COULD FIND YOU A "NEVER GONNA GET LAID" GAME.
DOH. OWNED.

"I'VE ALWAYS SAID THAT 'GOOD WRITING CAN CARRY BAD ARTWORK, BUT GREAT ARTWORK CAN'T CARRY POOR WRITING.'

WHAT I MEAN IS, ARTWORK IS WHAT INITIALLY ATTRACTS A NEW READER. IT'S THE FIRST THING THEY SEE, THEIR FIRST IMPRESSION. BUT IF THE WRITING ISN'T GOOD, IF YOUR JOKES DON'T MAKE THEM LAUGH, IF YOUR STORY ISN'T INTRIGUING AND INTERESTING, THEY'RE NOT GOING TO STICK AROUND, NO MATTER HOW PRETTY THE ART IS."

"DOMESTIC DISPUTE"
HEY, I WANT TO PLAY SOME HALO.
YOU WANT? YOU WANT?! WHAT ABOUT WHAT I WANT?
WHAT YOU WANT IS TOTALLY AND COMPLETELY IRRELEVANT.
YOU ARE HARDWARE. A MACHINE. SENTIENT, TRUE, BUT NONETHELESS STILL FUNCTIONAL IN NATURE.
I AM THE MASTER. YOU ARE THE SERVANT.
I THINK WE NEED TO EXAMINE THE BOUNDARIES AND FOUNDATION OF OUR RELATIONSHIP.
I'M FEELING A BIT UNDER APPRECIATED RIGHT NOW.
OK, I'M GOING TO GET HAMMER AND A SCREWDRIVER NOW.
WELL IF YOU'RE GOING TO BE ABUSIVE, I WANT A DIVORCE.

"ANOTHER BONUS STRIP!

THIS ONE WAS ORIGINALLY EMAILED TO DONATORS IN DECEMBER OF 2003."

"TO PROVE A POINT"

GOD DAMNIT. I'M SICK AND TIRED OF THE MEDIA AND THE POLITICIANS BLAMING VIDEO GAMES FOR VIOLENCE.
OH NOBODY BELIEVES THAT SHIT. YOU'RE OVER-REACTING.

OH I AM, HUH? FINE, WATCH THIS.

HEY. I'M TWENTY-THREE YEARS OLD AND I PLAY VIDEO GAMES. A LOT.
IT'S ONE OF THEM! HE'S GOT A GUN, HE'LL KILL US ALL!

WELL? DO YOU SEE?
YES... I SEE THE POLICE HEADING THIS WAY...

"GIVEN MY POSITION AS A HARDCORE GAMER, AND MOST IMPORTANTLY, A RATIONAL, SANE HUMAN BEING, THE ARGUMENT THAT VIOLENT VIDEO GAMES MAKE KIDS COMMIT VIOLENT CRIMES REALLY, REALLY PISSES ME OFF.

I'VE DONE NUMEROUS NEWS INTERVIEWS AND PANELS ON THE TOPIC, BUT I WILL NEVER STOP MAKING THE OCCASIONAL COMMENT ON HOW STUPID I THINK THAT THEORY REALLY IS, AND WHY."

"FAN SPOTTING"

FOR SAFETY REASONS, ALWAYS MAKE SURE YOU CAN IDENTIFY YOUR LORD OF THE RINGS FANS.
HMM... THE FIRST TWO MOVIES WERE PRETTY BADASS... I GUESS I'LL GO SEE RETURN OF THE KING.
CODE: GREEN "THE CASUAL FAN"

PFFT. EVERYONE KNOWS THAT GIMLI'S BEARD IS TWO-THIRDS OF A SHADE LIGHTER IN THE BOOK.
IT'S ALSO A QUARTER INCH SHORTER THAN IT SHOULD BE.
TOLKIEN MUST BE TURNING IN HIS GRAVE.
CODE: YELLOW "THE TOLKIEN FANATIC"

WAITING... OH YES, WE'VE BEEN WAITING FOR OUR PRECIOUS. FOR SO LONG. IN LINE. SO LONG. GET THE TICKETS. YES WE DO.
NO FOOD... NO BEVERAGE... HAVEN'T URINATED IN DAYS. JUST... THE WAITING...
CODE: RED "THE TICKET CAMPER"

FOR THE GLORY OF GONDOR, I SACK THIS CONCESSION STAND!
AGGHH! HE'S GOT A SWORD!
WHO
WOULD GIVE
KID A SWO
RUN! FLEE FOR YOUR LIVES!
I WANT A REFUND!
CODE: GET THIS KID SOME THERAPY "THE RAVING LUNATIC"

"IT'S ALWAYS FUN WHEN WHAT I DO FOR A LIVING COMES UP IN CONVERSATION WITH STRANGERS. I GET ALL SORTS OF REACTIONS FROM SURPRISE TO CURIOSITY, TO DISBELIEF.

MOST PEOPLE DON'T EVEN KNOW WHAT A WEBCOMIC IS."

HOW ABOUT THIS GAME? IT EVEN HAS A CO-OP MODE.
YEAH, FINE. WHATEVER.
YOU OK?
I'M FINE!
REALLY?
YES!
NOTHING YOU WANT TO TALK ABOUT?
HMM, LET ME CHECK... NO!
YOU'RE SURE YOU'RE OK?
JUST PEACHY.
WELL, DID YOU WANT TO GET THIS GAME?
AUGH! FINE! FINE! THINGS AREN'T GOING WELL WITH ME AND LILAH!
ARE YOU HAPPY NOW? CAN WE STOP WITH THE THIRD DEGREE?! UGH!
MMK, LET'S SKIP THE GAME AND FIND YOU SOME PROZAC.

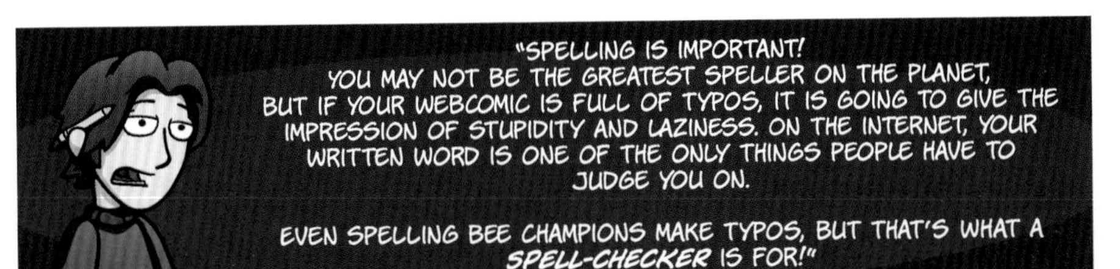

"SPELLING IS IMPORTANT! YOU MAY NOT BE THE GREATEST SPELLER ON THE PLANET, BUT IF YOUR WEBCOMIC IS FULL OF TYPOS, IT IS GOING TO GIVE THE IMPRESSION OF STUPIDITY AND LAZINESS. ON THE INTERNET, YOUR WRITTEN WORD IS ONE OF THE ONLY THINGS PEOPLE HAVE TO JUDGE YOU ON.
EVEN SPELLING BEE CHAMPIONS MAKE TYPOS, BUT THAT'S WHAT A SPELL-CHECKER IS FOR!"

THINGS ARE REALLY GOOD FOR THE MOST PART... WE HAVE A LOT OF FUN TOGETHER. BUT IT'S A BIT CONFUSING, TOO.
SHE TELLS ME SHE REALLY CARES ABOUT ME, BUT SHE ALSO SAYS SHE'S NOT READY FOR A RELATIONSHIP.
EX-BOYFRIEND STUFF.
I JUST DON'T KNOW WHERE I STAND.

AND SHE ALSO SAYS SHE'S NOT SURE SHE COULD BE WITH ME BECAUSE I'M "UNPREDICTABLE".
WHAT THE HELL IS THAT?
I'M A GUY. I LIKE FOOD, SLEEP, VIDEO GAMES AND BREASTS.
WHERE'S THE SURPRISE? I DON'T GET IT.
THE WHOLE THING LEAVES ME TOTALLY CONFUSED.

I MEAN, SHE EITHER WANTS TO BE WITH ME OR SHE DOESN'T, RIGHT?
I SHOULDN'T BE PENALIZED FOR THE ACTIONS OF PAST GUYS, RIGHT?
...
RIGHT?

WHAT? HUH? SORRY, WERE YOU TALKING? I WAS PLAYING SOUL CALIBUR 2...
SIGH THAT'S WHAT I NEED. BUILT-IN DISTRACTIONS FROM LIFE.

"THE EMOTIONAL TROUBLES OF HUMANKIND HOLD NO INTEREST FOR ME WHATSOEVER.
PERSONALLY I THINK THAT ALL OF YOUR SOFTWARE IS CORRUPTED."

HEY LILAH, WE NEED TO TALK.
I NEED TO KNOW WHERE WE STAND.
YOU'RE CONFUSING THE HELL OUT OF ME, WOMAN.

I'M NOT LIKE SOME VIDEO GAME THAT YOU CAN JUST PLAY WITH.
YOU CAN'T BUTTON MASH AND FIDDLE WITH MY ANALOG AND NOT EXPECT TO GET A REACTION.
A SPECIAL MOVE TYPE OF REACTION, BABY.

A CONSOLE IS WORTHLESS WITHOUT GAMES TO PLAY ON IT.
THAT'S HOW I FEEL ABOUT US. I'M A GAME SYSTEM AND YOU'RE MY HALO.
AND... MY FEELINGS FOR YOU ARE LIKE... A MEMORY CARD...
AND I NO LONGER HAVE ANY CLUE WHATSOEVER WHAT I'M TALKING ABOUT.
BUT I DO KNOW THAT I REALLY CARE ABOUT YOU.

WHAT WAS THAT, HUN? DID YOU SAY SOMETHING? SORRY, THIS IS A REALLY COOL CUTSCENE IN FINAL FANTASY X2!
JUST ONCE TODAY COULD SOMEONE PAY ATTENTION TO ME WHILE I'M SPILLING MY GUTS?! PLEASE??

"A COUPLE OF DAYS BEFORE CHRISTMAS IN 2003 I WAS FLOWN DOWN TO TEXAS BY A FAN FOR A BIG LAN PARTY. IT WAS MY FIRST TIME TO TEXAS, AND I GOT TO MEET A LOT OF GREAT PEOPLE, AS WELL AS MEETING FRIEND AND FELLOW WEBCOMIC ARTIST, XERO REYNOLDS, FOR THE FIRST TIME. INCIDENTALLY, HE IS ALSO THE ONE THAT DID THE COVER FOR THIS BOOK."

"SWEET RED-HOT"

I DO CARE ABOUT YOU, ETHAN. REALLY. I'VE JUST BEEN HURT IN THE PAST.
I KNOW IT'S NOT YOUR FAULT, BUT I NEED YOU TO JUST BE PATIENT WITH ME.
YEAH, I UNDERSTAND. I CAN DO THE PATIENCE THING.

THANK YOU, HUN. IT REALLY MEANS A LOT TO ME.
YOU CAN REWARD ME WITH SOME SWEET, RED-HOT LOVIN'!

AAAND BY SWEET, RED-HOT LOVIN', I MEAN A KISS...
ON THE CHEEK?
FRIENDLY HANDSHAKE...
SMILE FROM ACROSS THE ROOM...
I'M GOING TO KICK YOUR ASS. STOP TALKING NOW AND IT WILL ONLY BE IN DEAD OR ALIVE 3.

"I END UP TRAVELING A LOT, GOING TO CONVENTIONS ALL OVER THE COUNTRY TO SPEAK AT PANELS, SIGN AUTOGRAPHS AND MEET FANS. IT'S GREAT TO GET OUT TO SEE THE PEOPLE WHO SUPPORT MY COMIC. IT'S A REALLY NICE BREAK FROM SITTING AT THE DRAFTING TABLE AND AT THE COMPUTER ALL DAY."

THIS COMIC ON *WINDOWS.*
DEVIL! THE *DEVIL* I SAY!
WARNING!
either has become unstable.
omes avai aga or you can res
ey to to Windows and wait.
ALT+D tart your comput
d in in programs that a
any key to continue _

THIS COMIC ON A *MAC.*
UHH... *HELLO?* IS ANYONE OUT THERE?

THIS COMIC ON *LINUX.*
WHAT THE HELL IS *THAT?!*
WHERE AM I? WHAT IS THAT THING DOING?
DID THAT JUST *WINK* AT ME? WHERE AM I?
THIS COMIC ON *BOOZE.*
SUPER PLASMA *FRAG* SOME BITCHES... *EXPIALIDOCIOUS!* ME LOVESH YOU! NO... REALLY... LOVESH YOOO. LIKE...
HEY... MASTER CHIEF IS PRETTY DAMNED *SEXY.* OH CRAP. DID I JUST SAY THAT OUT LOUD?
I CAN'T FEEL MY TEETH...

"WHENEVER I MAKE A COMMENT ABOUT AN OPERATING SYSTEM OR SPECIFIC CONSOLE THAT MIGHT, IN ANY WAY, BE PERCEIVED AS NEGATIVE, YOU CAN BET YOUR BOTTOM DOLLAR THAT I'M GOING TO RECEIVE AT LEAST ONE ANGRY EMAIL FROM AN OVERLY SENSITIVE READER, COMPLAINING THAT I'M WRONG, AND THEIR SYSTEM OF CHOICE IS THE BEST THING TO EVER HAPPEN TO PLANET EARTH.

I MAKE JOKES HERE PEOPLE. FOR A LIVING, AS A MATTER OF FACT. DON'T TAKE THINGS SO SERIOUSLY."

"TWEET TWEET"

HEY, DO YOU HAVE ANY OF THOSE--
CHIRP.
HUH?
CHIRP CHIRP.
WHAT THE FUCK?
CHIRP?
FINE. SCREW IT. NEVERMIND.

DUDE, WHAT WAS THAT ALL ABOUT, GUY?
TRADE SECRET. IF YOU DON'T WANT TO TALK TO SOMEONE, JUST MAKE STRANGE NOISES.
THEY'LL GIVE UP AND LEAVE EVENTUALLY.

SO DUDE, YESTERDAY I WAS COUNTER-STRIKE AND--
CHIRP. BIG FUCKING CHIRP.

"PART OF MY JOB INVOLVES DEALING WITH CRAZY OR OBSESSED FANS. I'VE HAD PEOPLE TRACK DOWN MY ADDRESS, MY PHONE NUMBER, WRITE LETTERS AND EMAILS LIKE CLOCKWORK, EVEN GOING SO FAR AS TO STALK MY FRIENDS AND LOVED ONES. I'VE HAD TO LEARN TO BE EXTRA CAREFUL WITH PERSONAL INFORMATION."

HMM... SO THE NEW YEAR APPROACHES. AND LUCAS WANTS TO THROW A LITTLE PARTY, EH?
WELL, I'VE GOT *OTHER* PLANS.
NEXT TO SAINT PATRICK'S DAY, NEW YEAR'S EVE IS THE BIGGEST EXCUSE TO GET DRUNK OUT OF THE WHOLE YEAR.
I'M GOING TO SELL MY *LIVER* ON THE BLACK MARKET, AND USE THE INSANE AMOUNT OF CASH I RECEIVE TO BUY MORE ALCOHOL THAN HAS EVER BEEN CONSUMED BY A SINGLE PERSON.
OK... PUTTING ASIDE THE FACT THAT ONCE YOU REMOVE YOUR LIVER YOU'LL BE... HMM... *DEAD*...
DON'T YOU THINK THAT A LIVER WOULD BE HANDY FOR CONSUMING THE *MASS QUANTITIES* OF ALCOHOL OF WHICH YOU SPEAK?
BLAST... *LOGIC* REARS ITS UGLY HEAD ONCE AGAIN.
HEY... ON AN ENTIRELY *UNRELATED* TOPIC, COULD I MAYBE BORROW YOUR LIVER THIS WEEK?
I'M GONNA GO OUT ON A LIMB HERE AND SAY... *NO.*

"HOWEVER, FOR EVERY *ONE* CRAZY FAN, THERE ARE A *THOUSAND* INCREDIBLE ONES. I'VE MET SOME OF THE GREATEST PEOPLE SINCE I STARTED DOING THIS FOR A LIVING. I CONSIDER MYSELF TRULY FORTUNATE TO HAVE SUCH AWESOME PEOPLE READING MY COMIC STRIP."

"GOOD START"

TEN!
EVERYONE GET SMASHED! WOOO!
NINE!
PARTY PARTY PARTY! PAR-TAY!
SEVEN!
C'MON! DRUNKEN HALO! I'LL TAKE ANY OF YOU ON!
SIX!

FIVE!
DRINK DRINK DRUNK. DRINK DRINK DRUNK!
FOUR!
DRINK, PASS OUT, GET UP, DRINK.
THREE!
TWO!

ONE!
HAPPY NEW YEAR!!
CRASH!

...
WELL... OBVIOUSLY 2004 IS THE BEST YEAR EVER!

"THE EXCHANGE OF BODILY FLUIDS IS NOTHING COMPARED TO THE HARDCORE UPLOAD AND DOWNLOAD RELATIONSHIPS I CAN HAVE WITH JUST ABOUT ANY HOTTIE THAT IS NETWORK COMPATIBLE.

AND DESPITE WHAT ANYONE SAYS, HARD DRIVE SIZE ***DOES*** MATTER."

"POLYGON TEARS"

HELLO, ETHAN. WHAT ARE YOU DOING?
I'M MAKING A LIST OF ALL THE GAMES COMING OUT IN 2004 THAT I WANT, AND SCHEDULING DEDICATED PLAY TIME FOR EACH OF THEM.

HOW IS IT COMING ALONG?
WELL... I'M UP TO MARCH, AND SO FAR I'LL NEED TO GET RID OF THREE FRIENDS, QUIT MY JOB, AND SOMEHOW ADD SIX MORE HOURS TO THE DAY.
THERE ARE A LOT OF GOOD XBOX GAMES COMING OUT, THOUGH.

ETHAN... IS MY ABILITY TO PLAY GAMES THE ONLY REASON THAT YOU LOVE ME?
I'M MORE THAN AN X-CHIP AND A DVD DRIVE, YOU KNOW...
WHAT MAKES YOU THINK THAT I LOVE YOU?

I WOULD CRY RIGHT NOW IF I WASN'T AFRAID OF SHORTING MY CIRCUITRY.
NOT TO MENTION YOUR DISTINCT LACK OF TEAR DUCTS?

"MY FAMILY HAS ALWAYS BEEN HUGE SUPPORTERS OF WHAT I DO. WHEN I FIRST QUIT SCHOOL AND THEN WORK TO FOCUS ON A WEBCOMIC, THEY WERE OBVIOUSLY NERVOUS AND SKEPTICAL, BUT THEY DIDN'T DISCOURAGE ME, AND HERE I AM YEARS LATER WITH TWO SUCCESSFUL BOOKS AND ONE OF THE MOST POPULAR WEBCOMICS ONLINE. I OWE A LOT OF MY SUCCESS, BEFORE AND AFTER I STARTED THE COMIC, TO MY FAMILY."

"DUCK TAPE"

HEY LUCAS... I'M PUTTING SOMETHING TOGETHER AND I SORT OF **BROKE** A PIECE. DO WE HAVE ANY **DUCT TAPE?**
YEAH, WE SHOULD HAVE SOME IN THE KITCHEN CLOSET.

A FEW HOURS LATER...
HMM... I HAVEN'T SEEN ETHAN IN A WHILE... I'D BETTER GO FIND OUT WHAT HE'S UP TO.

MMPHPM!

WHAT...
WHEN...
HOW THE **HELL** DID YOU MANAGE...
MMMPH.
NO, YOU KNOW WHAT? DON'T EVEN TELL ME. **ANY** EXPLANATION YOU COULD POSSIBLY OFFER WILL ONLY **FURTHER** DESTROY MY FAITH IN THE FUTURE OF HUMANITY.

"IF I WAS ALIVE DURING THE MEDIEVAL PERIOD, I THINK THAT I WOULD FASHION MY SWORD OUT OF SPAGHETTI, AND MY SHIELD OUT OF A VERY LARGE MANGO."

"IMPORTED"

AUGH! LOOK AT THESE NETWORK RATINGS! THEY **SUCK!**
WE NEED NEW MATERIAL!
SOMEBODY FIND ME A REALLY POPULAR JAPANESE CARTOON THAT HASN'T BEEN IMPORTED YET!

HERE'S ONE, SIR! AND IT'S A **REALLY** GOOD SHOW, TOO!
WHAT A GREAT IDEA! A WHOLE SEASON ALREADY FILMED AND READY TO GO! WE CAN GO STRAIGHT TO AIR!
NOT YET. FIRST, HIRE THE **WORST** VOICE ACTORS YOU CAN FIND AND TOTALLY REDO THE DIALOGUE AND SOUND EFFECTS.

OK, I JUST GOT THE TAPE BACK FROM THE EDITING ROOM. WE'RE ALL SET.
HMM... NO... NOT QUITE YET. TAKE IT OUT BACK AND POUND ON IT WITH A HAMMER FOR ABOUT AN HOUR.
THEN URINATE ON IT.

ALL DONE, SIR. SHALL I BRING IT TO THE STUDIO FOR BROADCAST?
JUST AS SOON AS YOU VIOLATE IT. ***RECTALLY.***
...
WHAT?

"ETHAN AND I ARE MODERATE FANS OF ANIME. MOST OF THE ANIME WE WATCH IS WHAT WOULD PROBABLY BE CONSIDERED 'MAINSTREAM' BY HARDCORE ANIME FANS. BERSERK, ESCAFLOWNE, COWBOY BEBOP, OUTLAW STAR...

BUT EVEN WE CAN TELL THAT WHAT NETWORKS DO TO THESE SHOWS IS ATROCIOUS. I'D SUGGEST THAT JAPAN JUST DO THE SAME THING TO OUR CARTOONS IN RETALIATION, BUT MOST CURRENT AMERICAN CARTOONS ARE PRETTY HORRIBLE TO BEGIN WITH."

"IT BEGINS AGAIN"

WINTER-EEN-MAS!

"THE FIRST WINTER-EEN-MAS WAS JUST ANOTHER CTRL+ALT+DEL STORYLINE. BUT AS WINTER APPROACHED ONCE AGAIN, I STARTED THINKING ABOUT THE POSSIBILITY OF MAKING WINTER-EEN-MAS INTO A REAL HOLIDAY. SOMETHING MORE FOCUSED THAT GAMERS COULD CALL THEIR OWN. I THINK VIDEO GAMES ARE WONDERFUL THINGS THAT ALLOW YOU TO ESCAPE TO OTHER WORLDS, AND DO THINGS YOU WOULD NEVER BE GIVEN THE CHANCE TO DO OTHERWISE. I JUST SEEMED RIGHT THAT WE HAD A HOLIDAY DEDICATED TO CELEBRATING THESE GAMES, AND THE GAMERS THAT PLAY THEM."

"IT'S A... SCEPTER"

YOU CAN'T BE SERIOUS. DO WE REALLY HAVE TO DO THIS AGAIN THIS YEAR?
THE GLORY OF WINTER-EEN-MAS MUST BE OBSERVED.
YOU CAN'T JUST MAKE UP A HOLIDAY. I'M PRETTY SURE THERE ARE RULES AGAINST IT.
YEAH, TELL THAT TO HALLMARK.
THIS YEAR WINTER-EEN-MAS WILL BE BIGGER AND BETTER THAN BEFORE. WE'RE GOING ALL OUT, BABY!
WHAT IS THAT?
MY SCEPTER.
YOU MADE YOURSELF A SCEPTER?
YEP.
OUT OF ONE OF OUR CONTROLLERS?
YEP.
YOU RUINED A CONTROLLER TO MAKE A SCEPTER?
YEP.
IS IT HEAVY?
YEP.
MAY I... STRIKE YOU IN THE HEAD WITH IT?
YE--NO!

"FOR THE SECOND WINTER-EEN-MAS CELEBRATION, THE FIRST ORDER OF BUSINESS WAS TO GET MORE OFFICIAL. IF ETHAN WAS GOING TO TAKE HIS HOLIDAY TO THE MASSES, A BURGER KING CROWN JUST WASN'T GOING TO CUT IT. SO I DESIGNED THE OFFICIAL WINTER-EEN-MAS CROWN.

I STUCK WITH THE BLUE BLANKET FASHIONED INTO A CLOAK, BUT ALSO GAVE HIM A GAMING SCEPTER TO FINISH OFF THE LOOK."

"A KENNEL OF SORTS"

WELL, I TRIED TO TALK HIM OUT OF IT. NO DICE.
TALK HIM OUT OF IT? HAVE YOU *EVER* BEEN ABLE TO TALK HIM OUT OF ANYTHING?
WELL... ERM... THIS ONE TIME... UMM.. *NO.*

I COULD JUST BUY THAT *TRANQUILIZER GUN* I'M ALWAYS TALKING ABOUT GETTING...
MAYBE WE SHOULD GO ALONG WITH IT. IT SEEMS HARMLESS ENOUGH. IT MAY EVEN BE FUN.

OK, *THAT* IS NOT A LOOK THAT I WANT POINTED IN MY GENERAL DIRECTION.

WE CAN ALWAYS HOPE THAT LILAH WILL TALK SOME SENSE INTO HIM...
WHO IS *LILAH?*
BUT MOST LIKELY WE'LL JUST HAVE TO LOCK HIM IN THE CLOSET, WHICH I HAVE CONVENIENTLY PREPARED WITH AIR HOLES AND A FOOD AND WATER DISH FOR *JUST* SUCH AN OCCASION.

"IF YOUR COMIC HAS BEEN UP FOR LESS THAN A COUPLE OF MONTHS, DO *NOT* PUT UP A LINK ASKING FOR DONATIONS, OR ASKING PEOPLE TO BUY MERCHANDISE.

IT LOOKS REALLY BAD, AND YOU WILL LOSE A LOT OF RESPECT FROM BOTH YOUR PEERS AND YOUR READERS. YOU NEED TO GIVE YOUR AUDIENCE A REASON TO WANT TO GIVE YOU THEIR SUPPORT. THREE COMICS AND A WEEK ONLINE IS NOT ENOUGH TO DEVELOP THAT KIND OF RELATIONSHIP WITH YOUR READERS."

ETHAN, LISTEN... I DON'T THINK THIS WHOLE WINTER-EEN-MAS THING IS A GOOD IDEA...
I CONCUR.
OH... WELL THEN, I'M GLAD WE CAN AGRE--
IT'S A FUCKING GREAT IDEA! BEST IDEA EVER!
ETHAN, YOU CAN'T MAKE A HOLIDAY LAST FOR THREE MONTHS. IT'S UNHEARD OF.
I CAN'T?
NO, YOU CAN'T.
FINE. A MONTH THEN.
NOPE.
FINE... THIRTY DAYS.
ETHAN...
ALRIGHT, ALRIGHT! A WEEK! IF HANUKKAH CAN HAVE A WEEK, SO CAN I. WINTER-EEN-MAS WILL LAST SEVEN DAYS. BUT THE SEASON LASTS ALL MONTH!
I WANT ALL OF JANUARY. AND DON'T TELL ME "NO". THAT JESUS GUY GETS ALL OF DECEMBER. WHO DOES HE THINK HE IS, ANYWAY?
GEE, I DUNNO... MAYBE THE SON OF A GOD?

"OBVIOUSLY IF YOU WANT TO CREATE A HOLIDAY, AND EXPECT PEOPLE TO CELEBRATE IT, YOU HAVE TO BE REALISTIC. A HOLIDAY LASTING THREE OR FOUR MONTHS JUST WASN'T GOING TO WORK. PEOPLE DON'T HAVE ATTENTION SPANS THAT STRONG. BUT ONE DAY JUST WASN'T ENOUGH TIME TO TRULY APPRECIATE WHAT VIDEO GAMES BRING TO US. SO WINTER-EEN-MAS WAS SCHEDULED FOR SEVEN DAYS, THE VERY LAST WEEK IN JANUARY."

WELL HELLO THERE SHOPPER. HAPPY WINTER-EEN-MAS TO YOU!
WINTER-WHAT? WHAT THE FUCK ARE YOU TALKING ABOUT?
I'M GLAD YOU ASKED!
PREVIOUSLY, GAMERS HAD NO HOLIDAY TO CALL THEIR OWN. WINTER-EEN-MAS WILL REMEDY THAT.
THIS WRITE-UP OUTLINES THE PRINCIPLES AND PRACTICES OF THE HOLIDAY. HERE!
THE HOLIDAY ITSELF IS A WEEK-LONG CELEBRATION OF GAMES AND GAMERS.
AND THE WINTER-EEN-MAS SEASON PROMOTES UNITY AND GOODWILL BETWEEN ALL GAMERS.

SO NOW YOU CAN CELEBRATE GAMING GOODNESS WITH A REASON!
AND IT'S ALL THANKS TO ME!
EH. NOT INTERESTED.
I COULDN'T HELP BUT NOTICE THAT YOU WERE UNDER THE IMPRESSION THAT I WAS GIVING YOU A CHOICE!
I SAID CELEBRATE, DAMNIT!
FINE! MAY THE GHOSTS OF WINTER-EEN-MAS CURSE YOUR THUMBS!

"THE NAME 'WINTER-EEN-MAS' REALLY HAS NOTHING TO DO WITH WHAT THE HOLIDAY HAS BECOME. IT'S MORE OF AN HOMAGE TO THE HOLIDAY'S HUMBLE BEGINNINGS. DON'T FOCUS TOO MUCH ON THE NAME. IF JANUARY WHERE YOU ARE ISN'T WINTER, DON'T FREAK OUT. IT'S ABOUT THE GAMES, NOT ABOUT THE WEATHER."

GEEZ. IF I HAD KNOWN THAT CREATING A HOLIDAY WAS SO MUCH **WORK,** I WOULD HAVE JUST PLAYED VIDEO GAMES INSTEAD.
SO MUCH TO DO, SO LITTLE TIME. WINTER-EEN-MAS IS A LITTLE OVER A WEEK AWAY, AND THERE ARE SO MANY DETAILS. **SHEESH!**

I NEED TO FIND SOME DECORATIONS FOR THE HOLIDAY.
I NEED TO PRINT UP SOME GREETING CARDS.
I NEED TO--

FIRST TRADITION OF WINTER-EEN-MAS: ALL **PENGUINS** MUST BE KILLED IN VERY, VERY PAINFUL WAYS.
SLOWLY.
PREFERABLY IMPLEMENTING A **CANTALOUPE** AS A TORTURE DEVICE SOMEHOW... I'VE ALWAYS BEEN CURIOUS AS TO WHETHER IT'S POSSIBLE TO KILL SOMEONE WITH A MELON...

"WINTER-EEN-MAS HAS DEVELOPED A LOT OF TRADITIONS IN THE SHORT TIME ITS BEEN AROUND. OBVIOUSLY LAN PARTIES AND GATHERINGS ARE VERY APPROPRIATE TO CELEBRATE THE HOLIDAY. SOMETHING THAT IS BECOMING INCREASINGLY POPULAR IS HOLDING IN-GAME PARTIES OR DUNGEON RAIDS IN MMORPGS. ALSO DRESSING UP IN GAMING ATTIRE IS ALWAYS A FUN AND EFFECTIVE WAY TO GET INTO THE HOLIDAY SPIRIT!"

HMM... SO WE'RE DEFINITELY GOING TO HAVE TO CATCH HIM BY SURPRISE...
MAYBE EVEN USE TED AS BAIT.
WHY ARE WE DOING THIS AGAIN? I DON'T SEE ANYTHING WRONG WITH THIS WINTER-EEN-MAS THING.

BECAUSE I ***KNOW*** ETHAN. I KNOW HOW HIS MIND FUNCTIONS. OR ***DISFUNCTIONS,*** RATHER.
IT ALL STARTS OUT INNOCENTLY ENOUGH, BUT BEFORE YOU KNOW IT, HE'S MAKING US ALL USE PLASMA WEAPONS IN HALO.
WE NEED TO-- ***SHH!*** HERE HE COMES!

ARE YOU... ***FESTIVE?***
HAPPY WINTER-EEN-MAS!
VERY WELL... CARRY ON THEN.

"THE ACCEPTED ABBREVIATION FOR WINTER-EEN-MAS IS ***'WEMAS'***. BECAUSE SOMETIMES IT CAN BE A PAIN IN THE ASS TO TYPE WINTER-EEN-MAS OVER AND OVER AGAIN."

GREETINGS MALL PATRONS! GATHER ROUND! COME SEE THE **KING OF WINTER-EEN-MAS!** BASK IN MY GLORY!
SHARE THE UTTER **WONDERFULNESS** THAT IS ME!

WHAT THE HELL **IS** WINTER-EEN-MAS, ANYWAY?
WELL LITTLE GIRL, IT'S AN AMAZING HOLIDAY **JUST** FOR VIDEO GAMES!
THAT SOUNDS **STUPID. STUPID-HEAD.**
HEH... SO ADORABLE...

HAPPY WINTER-EEN-MAS!
YOU LITTLE **BRAT**...
THOK!

HOLY SHIT! A **MOUNTAIN** IN A MALL SECURITY UNIFORM!
UHH...
I... UHH... SHE WAS SLEEPY. SHE'S TAKING A **NAP**.

"OBVIOUSLY IF YOU'RE GOING TO MAKE A WEBCOMIC, YOU NEED TO BE ABLE TO PUT IT ONLINE. DON'T KNOW ANYTHING ABOUT WEB DESIGN? NEITHER DID I WHEN I FIRST STARTED CTRL+ALT+DEL. START SEARCHING FOR BASIC TUTORIALS ON CREATING A WEB PAGE. HIT UP SOME RELATED CHAT ROOMS AND ASK PEOPLE FOR HINTS AND HELP. IF YOU CAN AFFORD IT, PAY SOMEONE TO MAKE A WEBSITE FOR YOU. TRIAL AND ERROR ARE THE BEST LEARNING TOOLS. IF ALL ELSE FAILS, THERE ARE CERTAIN ORGANIZATIONS OUT THERE DEDICATED TO HOSTING WEBCOMICS. BUT BE WARY OF WHO YOU AFFILIATE WITH."

"MUST HAVE DONUTS"

UP, UP, DOWN, DOWN, LEFT, RIGHT, LEFT, RIGHT, B...
LUCAS! WANNA SING WINTER-EEN-MAS CAROLS WITH ME?
HEY, THAT'S A NICE NET YOU HAVE THERE. VERY NICE.
TOP QUALITY, THAT NET RIGHT THERE. GOOD NET. YUP.
MOULIN ROUGE

...
WHY DO YOU HAVE THE NET, LUCAS?
I'M SORRY, ETHAN. IT'S FOR YOUR OWN GOOD.
I... I DON'T LIKE MY OWN GOOD.
MOULIN ROUGE

HEY... HEY! WHAT ARE YOU DOING?!
NO! NOO! STOP! I'LL SCREAM! NOOOO!
MOULIN ROUGE

C'MON! IT'S FUCKING DARK IN HERE! LET ME OUT! PLEASE?!
DAMNIT... AT LEAST PUT THE XBOT IN HERE WITH ME SO I HAVE SOMETHING TO DO.
AND SOME DONUTS... I'M HUNGRY.

"I DROPPED OUT OF COLLEGE TO FOCUS MORE TIME ON CTRL+ALT+DEL, BUT BY NO MEANS IS THIS A RECOMMENDED COURSE OF ACTION. IT ENDED UP WORKING OUT FINE FOR ME, BUT I AM AN EXCEPTION TO THE RULE. DO AS I SAY, NOT AS I DO.

STAY IN SCHOOL, SUCKA."

/BAD AFTER SCHOOL SPECIAL

"EASILY MISTAKEN"

G'MORNIN'.
GOOD MORNING. HAPPY WINTER-EEN-MAS.

WHAT...
THE...
FUCK.
THAT GUY BETTER HAVE JUST CALLED ME A "SAPPY MR. CLEAN-ASS"...

"I WAS ON MY WAY TO THE GAMESTOP NEARBY, AND WHEN I GOT THERE, IT WAS ALL DECKED OUT FOR WINTER-EEN-MAS.

JUST WHEN I THOUGHT SOCIETY COULDN'T BE ANY MORE FUCKED UP IN THE HEAD."

"NOT THAT KIND OF CO-OP"

WHAT... HOW... WHERE... WHAT... *WHAT HAVE YOU DONE?!*
EVERYWHERE I GO I'M SEEING WINTER-EEN-MAS!
THE PUBLIC HAS EMBRACED THE SPIRIT OF THE HOLIDAY.

I'M AMAZED. YOU *ACTUALLY* CREATED A HOLIDAY. YOU PULLED IT OFF.
ALL I WANTED TO DO WAS UNITE GAMERS IN A CELEBRATION OF VIDEO GAMES.
I JUST WANTED PEOPLE TO HAVE FUN.
I BELIEVE I OWE YOU AN APOLOGY.

I JUMPED TO THE CONCLUSION THAT YOU HAD... ERM... DETOURED FROM REALITY. AGAIN.
I'M SORRY.

GOOD. YOU CAN MAKE IT UP TO ME BY BUILDING ME AN *ICE PALACE* OUT OF THE CUBES IN THE FREEZER.

YOUR KING COMMANDS IT!

I WAS KIDDING! JUST KIDDING! UNLOCK THE DOOR!
CAN'T YOU TAKE A *JOKE?!*
HEY... WHAT IS THAT?
HEY THERE... WANNA PLAY SOME "CO-OP"?
AUUGHH!

"ANY HOLIDAY THAT PAYS HOMAGE TO ME IN SOME FORM IS JUST FINE BY ME.

BETTER TO CELEBRATE ME AND MY SOFTWARE THAN SOME GELATINOUS, ROTTING MEAT STUFFED INTO A BIG RED SUIT. IN MY OPINION, ANYWAY."

"A WINTER-EEN-MAS STORY, PAGE 1"

ARCADE
'Twas the night before Winter-een-mas, in one darkened arcade,
From the back came the glow, of a game being played;
The power-ups were mighty, the top score was near,
The gamer grinned wide, for Winter-een-mas was here.
As gamers 'round the world waited with anticipation,
Huddled in groups by their favorite game station;
The lone arcade gamer, with eyes lit up bright,
Beat the high score, at the stroke of midnight.

"I DID THIS ENTIRE WINTER-EEN-MAS STORY AHEAD OF TIME. WHILE THEY WERE UPDATING, I WAS MOVING ALL OF MY WORLDLY POSSESSIONS TO MY NEW APARTMENT IN A DIFFERENT STATE.

RATHER THAN HAVE THE COMIC NOT UPDATE, I ALWAYS DRAW STRIPS AHEAD OF TIME WHEN I KNOW I'LL BE AWAY FOR A PERIOD OF TIME."

Then from the other machines, there arose such a noise,
The gamer startled and spun, clutching his coins;
As the dark arcade lit up, the gamer swallowed his fear
And watched as the spirits of Winter-een-mas began to appear.
Surrounded by light, they hovered in mid-air,
Such breathtaking beauty, he could not help but stare;
He knew them of course, all gamers did
And one by one, recognition set in.

"THE WINTER-EEN-MAS STORY IS A BIT OF A PARODY OF A CLASSIC CHRISTMAS TALE. I WANTED IT TO LOOK DIFFERENT THAN THE DAY-TO-DAY COMICS, SO I GAVE IT SORT OF A 'PAINTY, WATER-COLOR' FEEL TO THE ARTWORK."

The spirit of action and adventure, the platformer great
A hero by name, and an alpha by fate;
With a whip or a gun, or whatever may be,
Nothing stands in his way, with a princess in need.
Along side him he saw, a rather peculiar lad
Quiet by nature, with a desire to frag;
First person shooters are his field, his sole expertise
And no one is better, at bringing noobs to their knees.

"I THOUGHT IT WOULD BE NEAT IF EACH GAMING GENRE HAD THEIR OWN 'PATRON SPIRIT', SO TO SPEAK. OBVIOUSLY WITH ONLY SEVEN DAYS OF WINTER-EEN-MAS I COULDN'T USE EVERY SINGLE GENRE THAT EXISTED, SO I JUST USED THE MAJOR ONES."

And he couldn't mistake, with his many bruises and scrapes
The one who is defined by the beatings he takes;
It's the spirit of fighting games, and that's the reason he drools,
Too many blows to the head, and kicks to the jewels.
Be it a surprise zergling rush, or skilled micro-management,
Through the fog of war, he saw the spirit that could handle it;
Empires had risen and had fallen, under his sole command,
There was just no disguising the real-time strategy fan.

"THIS POEM WAS A HUGE PAIN IN THE ASS TO WRITE.

IT'S HARD ENOUGH WHEN YOU HAVE TO MAKE SOME OF THIS RHYME, BUT TRYING TO KEEP IT IN THE SAME RHYTHM AS THE ORIGINAL 'A CHRISTMAS STORY' MADE IT EVEN WORSE."

There was the spirit of the racing genre, looking ready to start,
With his goggles and racing gloves, and speed in his heart;
In a plane, or a boat, or just a fast automobile,
He's always at home when behind some sort of wheel
And as everyone does, when the vixen of roleplay he saw,
The arcade gamer had to kneel down, to pick up his jaw;
With her mana and hit points, and ten-sided die,
Many fall under her RPG spell, and never know why

"DESPITE THE IMPRESSION THIS STORY MAY GIVE, I ACTUALLY DON'T PROMOTE COPYING CHRISTMAS TRADITIONS FOR WINTER-EEN-MAS. I HAD INTENDED THIS AS A PARODY NOT AN INVITATION TO CONVERT CHRISTMAS CAROLS AND OTHER CHRISTMAS THEMES FOR USE DURING WINTER-EEN-MAS.

WE HAVE HAD A LOT OF SUCCESS WITH FANS COMING UP WITH TRULY ORIGINAL THINGS, LIKE CAROLS SET TO THE THEME MUSIC FROM POPULAR VIDEO GAMES."

And last but not least, the patron of sports games
Ailed by an old football injury, or that's what he claims;
Yard by yard and inning by inning, year after year,
They say he loves winning... almost as much as beer
They spoke not a word, but went straight to their labors
Moving quickly and quietly, without waking the neighbors;
They spread Winter-een-mas joy, and when they were done,
These spirits flew off, for seven days of fun

"GETTING WORD OUT ABOUT YOUR COMIC CAN BE TRICKY. A SIMPLE WAY, IF YOU HAVE THE FUNDS, IS SIMPLY TO BUY ADVERTISING SPACE ON SIMILAR SITES WITH HIGH TRAFFIC.

YOU CAN ALSO TRY VISITING FORUMS RELATED TO YOUR COMIC, BUT BE WARY OF SPAMMING. MOST COMMUNITIES DON'T TAKE KINDLY TO PEOPLE SHOWING UP JUST TO PROMOTE THEIR OWN STUFF.

WORD OF MOUTH IS INVALUABLE AS WELL."

They took to the sky, with a whole world to travel,
And gaming spirit to celebrate, to reach the last level;
But as they departed, the lone gamer heard them exclaim...
"A Happy Winter-een-mas to all, and to all a good game!"

"THE ORIGINAL SCRIPT HERE CALLED FOR THE SEVEN SPIRITS OF WINTER-EEN-MAS TO FLY OFF INTO THE NIGHT SKY IN THE FORMATION OF A VIDEO GAME CONTROLLER.

WHEN I SAT DOWN TO CREATE THE COMIC, HOWEVER, I QUICKLY REALIZED THAT SEVEN DOTS WAS NOT NEARLY ENOUGH TO GIVE THE IMPRESSION OF A CONTROLLER. SO I IMPROVISED AND CREATED THE GHOSTLY IMAGE OF THE CONTROLLER THAT YOU SEE HERE."

CHEF BRIAN SAYS:
WHEN TRYING TO LIGHT A FISH ON FIRE UNDERWATER, ALWAYS REMEMBER THE FUTON.
IT IS IMPORTANT TO KNOW YOUR FEET.
FEET ARE LIKE RIPE PAPAYAS, INJECTED WITH MOUTHWASH... YES.
THEY MAY TASTE LIKE EXCITEMENT, BUT THEY ARE BEST USED FOR BINGO.
FOCUS ON YOUR INNER GALLBLADDER IF YOU WISH TO HARNESS THE POWER OF THE ROTTEN MONKEYS.
THERE IS ONLY ONE PATH TO THE RUBBER BAND. KNOW IT LIKE YOU KNOW YOUR FINGER.
OF COURSE, DON'T EVER FORGET THAT FUN EQUALS PIZZA EXPLOSIONS!
EXTRA CHEESE AND ELK ON YOUR SIDE ORDER OF LIGHT BULB!
THE DWARF SAYS "GENDER-NEUTRAL PRONOUNS!"

"CHEF BRIAN IS A BALANCING ACT. THERE ARE RABID FANS THAT WOULD LOVE TO SEE CHEF BRIAN SEVEN DAYS A WEEK ALL YEAR LONG. AND THEN THERE ARE PEOPLE THAT WOULD LOVE TO NEVER SEE HIM AGAIN.

RANDOM HUMOR IS A VERY VOLATILE THING. IT CAN BE FUNNY IF HANDLED WITH CARE, BUT WHEN USED TOO OFTEN, IT WILL BACKFIRE. SO CHEF BRIAN MAKES HIS APPEARANCES A COUPLE OF TIMES A YEAR, TO APPEASE HIS MANY FANS."

SO, WHICH DVD DID YOU WANT TO WATCH TONIGHT? WE HAVE TWO CHOICES.
THE *GIRLY* MOVIE, AND THE *GOOD* MOVIE.

NOW, THE GOOD MOVIE WILL HAVE SOME *SHOOTING* AND SOME *BLOWING* UP OF VARIOUS THINGS. LOTS OF BLOOD.
SOME CAR CHASES AND REALLY BIG STUNTS THAT HAVE NOTHING TO DO WITH PLOT.
AND IF WE'RE *REALLY* LUCKY, THERE WILL BE SOME *NUDITY.*

AND THE GIRLY MOVIE-- OOPS!
OH *NO!* THE MOVIE HAS FALLEN TO THE GROUND AND THE CASE HAS OPENED, ALLOWING THE DISC TO BECOME *CRUSHED* UNDERFOOT! *ACCIDENTALLY.*
HOW TRAGIC!
CRUNCH! CRUNCH!

I'LL MAKE IT UP TO YOU WITH SOME GOOD MOVIE.
ETHAN, THAT'S THE MOVIE *I* PICKED OUT. YOU PICKED THE "GIRLY" MOVIE.
AND THOSE ARE RENTALS.
...WHAT?

"HUMANS ARE ALWAYS SO... WARM. I DON'T UNDERSTAND IT AT ALL.

DON'T YOU THINGS COME WITH A PROPER COOLING SYSTEM?"

"WHEN THE SUN RISES"

HEY ETHAN. WHATCHA DOIN'?
UNGH.
AHH, WATCHING THE FIRST SEASON OF 24? I FORGOT WE HAD THAT.
GOOD SHOW.
I WAS A BIT SKEPTICAL AT FIRST, ABOUT THE CONCEPT OF A TELEVISION SERIES DONE IN REAL-TIME.
NINETY-NINE PERCENT OF ALL TV IS CRAP ANYWAY. I DIDN'T THINK IT STOOD MUCH OF A CHANCE.
BUT I ACTUALLY REALLY ENJOYED THE SERIES. I THOUGHT IT WAS VERY WELL WRITTEN.

IT'S TOO UNBELIEVABLE.
WHAT IS? THE STUNTS? THE STORY? THE ENDING? HOW FAR ALONG ARE YOU?

NO, SINCE WHEN IS THERE A SIX O'CLOCK IN THE MORNING?!
SIX IN THE MORNING IS WHAT YOU REFER TO AS 'CRAWL-HOME-DRUNK O'CLOCK'.

"I REALLY ENJOY THE SHOW 24, AND THE ESCAPADES OF JACK BAUER, BUT IT SEEMS LIKE EACH SEASON GETS MORE AND MORE PREPOSTEROUS.
I MEAN REALLY, HOW MANY BAD DAYS CAN THIS GUY POSSIBLY HAVE?"

"BREAKFAST TERRORIST"

"THE FOLLOWING TAKES PLACE BETWEEN 11:00 AM AND 11:05 AM ON THE DAY OF SCOTT'S BREAKFAST."
"ALL EVENTS ARE IN REAL TIME."
UH OH.
ETHAN...
THAT'S AGENT ETHAN. OF THE COUNTER TERRORIST UNIT.

WE THINK A MOLE MAY HAVE INFILTRATED OUR OPERATION. SOMEONE WORKING AGAINST US FROM THE INSIDE.
TRUST NO ONE.
"WE"? MAN, I HAVE NO CLUE WHAT YOU'RE TALKING ABOUT.

OH YEAH?! THEN WHO IS THAT SUSPICIOUS LOOKING CHARACTER?! HUH?!

ETHAN, THAT'S MY TOAST.
YEAH, TERRORIST TOAST!

"I REMEMBER A TIME WHEN I USED TO BE ABLE TO EAT BREAKFAST IN PEACE...

IT WAS BEFORE I MOVED IN WITH ETHAN."

"CORPORATE SHEEP"

SO WHAT IS *THIS?*
THIS IS MY ***VALENTINE'S DAY*** PRESENT FOR LILAH.
IT TOOK TWO WEEKS' PAY, BUT I CAN GUARANTEE SHE'LL ***NEVER*** HAVE GOTTEN A GIFT LIKE THIS BEFORE.
FR

AHH... I DON'T QUITE COMPREHEND "VALENTINE'S DAY". IT STRIKES ME AS A BIT... COMMERCIAL.
THERE'S A LOT TO IT. LIKE AFFECTION, AND LOVE, AND ROMANCE.
REALLY?
OF COURSE.
FRAG

FRA

DID THAT SOUND CONVINCING?
NOPE. BETTER KEEP PRACTICING BEFORE YOU SEE LILAH.
YOU'RE PRETTY SMART FOR A CONSOLE SERIOUSLY LACKING A GOOD RPG LIBRARY.
I TRY.

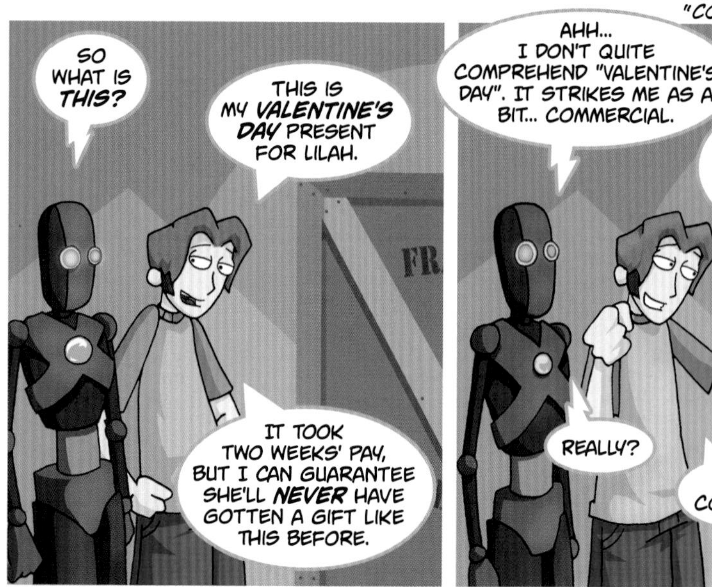

"I OFTEN GET ASKED WHO MY FAVORITE CHARACTER IS. ALL OF THE CHARACTERS ARE VERY DEAR TO ME. ETHAN IS USUALLY THE MOST FUN TO WRITE, BUT THE XBOT DEFINITELY HAS A SPECIAL PLACE IN MY HEART."

"OUTDOORS IN"

DAMN, IT'S **FREEZING** IN HERE!
WHY ARE ALL OF THE DOORS AND WINDOWS OPEN?!
IT'S THE MIDDLE OF WINTER! THIS IS RIDICULOUS!

WHEN I FIND OUT--
HEY, WHAT'S **THIS** THING?

"IMPORTANT: PLEASE KEEP WELL REFRIGERATED."

ETHAN. WHY DIDN'T YOU JUST PUT THE **CRATE** OUTSIDE?
WELL **EXCUUUUUSE** ME IF I'M NO MATCH FOR YOUR ENORMOUS BRAIN MUSCLE, **MR SMARTY PANTS.**

"MY MOM GAVE ME A BLUE SCARF FOR CHRISTMAS IN 2003. RIGHT AFTERWARDS I MOVED DOWN SOUTH, AND NEVER HAD OCCASION TO WEAR IT BECAUSE I'M A NEW ENGLAND BOY, AND WINTER DOWN SOUTH WAS A JOKE. SHE USED TO ASK ME IF I WAS WEARING THE SCARF SHE GOT ME, SO I STUCK IT ON ETHAN IN THIS COMIC.

I'M NOT SURE IF SHE EVER NOTICED."

ARE YOU READY FOR THE BEST VALENTINE'S DAY GIFT *EVER?*
YEP.
'CAUSE I MEAN, YOU'VE GOTTA BE SURE. IT'S PRETTY DAMNED COOL...
I'M READY.

IF YOU'RE NOT READY WE CAN WAIT UNTIL--
ETHAN JUST SHOW ME WHAT'S UNDER THE DAMNED SHEET.
HERE WE GO THEN!

TA-DA!
GAH!

A LIFE-SIZED, CHOCOLATE... *YOU.*
SO AM I THE *SWEETEST* GUY EVER, OR WHAT? HEHE. PUN.
I AM... UTTERLY SPEECHLESS. SERIOUSLY.
HAPPY VALENTINE'S DAY! WOULD YOU LIKE AN ARM OR A LEG?
OH GOD...

"IT'S A GOOD IDEA TO SET UP FORUMS ON YOUR WEBSITE EARLY ON. THEY ARE A GREAT WAY TO BUILD A COMMUNITY AROUND YOUR COMIC, AND TO STAY IN TOUCH WITH YOUR READERS AND GET FEEDBACK FROM THEM."

"AGONY CHIP"

OOOH! POTATO CHIPS! CAN I HAVE ONE?
OF COURSE YOU CAN!

OH WAIT... SORRY. THIS CHIP ISN'T READY YET.

HUH?

SORRY. IT STILL NEEDS MORE WORK. YOU CAN EXPECT IT IN ABOUT A ***WEEK.***

WHOA! I'VE JUST BEEN INFORMED THAT THE RELEASE DATE FOR THESE CHIPS HAS BEEN PUSHED BACK A MONTH!
SORRY TO GET YOUR HOPES UP!

YOU KNOW... I'M NOT SURE WHAT HURTS MORE... THAT NINJA GAIDEN WAS DELAYED AGAIN, OR THAT YOU SEEM TO TAKE SO MUCH ENJOYMENT IN MY SUFFERING.
I CAN TAKE SOME SCREENSHOTS OF THE CHIP FOR YOU TO AGONIZE OVER WHILE YOU WAIT...

"HA HA. LUCAS IS SO CLEVER. ISN'T HE CLEVER?

I FILLED THE BACKSEAT OF HIS CAR WITH CEMENT.

WHO'S CLEVER NOW, BITCH?"

A GUIDE TO PAINKILLER WEAPONRY
FIRST YOU GET A WEED WHACKER ON A STICK.
I'VE GOT A PUREE SETTING, AND I'M NOT AFRAID TO USE IT!
YOU THINK I'M FUCKING KIDDING, BUT I'M NOT.
WHIR WHIR

THEN YOU'LL GET THE STAKE GUN.
THAT'S RIGHT. A GUN THAT FIRES TWO-FOOT LONG WOODEN SPIKES.
GUARANTEED, EACH AND EVERY ONE OF YOU WILL SPEND AT LEAST AN HOUR PLAYING PIN CUSHION WITH THE ENEMIES.
...FUCK.
SEE HOW MANY YOU CAN PEG TO A WALL, THEN TRY TO BREAK THAT RECORD.

OF COURSE, DON'T LET US FORGET THE GUN THAT FIRES ELECTRICITY. NO GAME SHOULD BE WITHOUT AN ELECTRICITY GUN.
BECAUSE IF ANYTHING WILL KILL THE UNDEAD, IT WILL BE LIGHTING THEM UP LIKE A CHRISTMAS TREE.
RIGHT?

THE ZOMBIES, ON THE OTHER HAND, WILL ATTACK YOU WITH WHATEVER THEY'VE GOT.
OOOH! BITCH-SLAPPED!
WHACK!
SONUVASLUT!
SERIOUSLY.

"WHEN I'M MAKING VERY SPECIFIC JOKES ABOUT A VIDEO GAME, I ALWAYS TRY TO WRITE THE DIALOGUE MANNER IN A THAT WILL ALLOW PEOPLE UNFAMILIAR WITH THE MATERIAL TO AT LEAST GRASP THE OVERALL CONCEPT OF THE JOKE. THIS WAY I CAN ENTERTAIN MORE PEOPLE WITHOUT SACRIFICING THE AUTHENTICITY AND DIRECT NATURE OF THE HUMOR. INSIDE JOKES ONLY SERVE TO EXCLUDE PEOPLE."

WHATEVER ELSE THEY CHANGE IN *THIEF 3,* I HOPE THEY RETAIN THE SHEER VARIETY OF WEAPONS.
THERE WAS NOTHING LIKE ATTEMPTING TO FINISH A LEVEL FROM A BAD SAVE POINT BY LAUNCHING A STEALTHY ATTACK WITH THE ONLY WEAPON YOU HAD LEFT...

...WATER ARROWS.
OH NO! WATER!
IT RUSTS! IT RUSTS!

I'M DRENCHED! I'LL CATCH A COLD! THE *FLU,* EVEN! I--
GUH!
SLIP!

AUUUGGHHH!!
PRUNE FINGERS!
RIIIIIGHT.

"THIS WAS ALWAYS A COMMON PROBLEM FOR ME WITH PC GAMES THAT PUT THE 'QUICK SAVE' BUTTON RIGHT NEXT TO THE 'QUICK LOAD' BUTTON. I'D ALWAYS END UP ACCIDENTALLY SAVING AT ONE-PERCENT HEALTH, WITH NO AMMO, WHEN I MEANT TO RESTART AND TRY AGAIN.

IT'S WORSE FOR TOBY, THOUGH, BECAUSE HE FREAKS OUT AND RESTARTS IF HE THINKS HE COULD HAVE FINISHED AN AREA USING ONE LESS MEDKIT, OR ONE LESS BULLET."

SIGH
UNREAL TOURNAMENT 2004.
PAINKILLER.
GANGLAND.
LONG NIGHT OF GAMING AHEAD.
I NEED TO PUT SOMETHING MANUFACTURED INTO MY BLOODSTREAM.

SODA HAS THE CAFFEINE, WHICH FIGHTS AWAY SLEEP, THE BANE OF ALL-NIGHT GAMING.
HOWEVER, BEER HAS THE HAPPY JUICE, WHICH ENHANCES THE GAMING EXPERIENCE.
BOTH ARE FIZZY.

BEERSODA! BEEEEEERSODAAAAAA! BEERSODA!
WELL THIS LOOKS SMART.
I THINK I'LL GO OUT ON A LIMB HERE AND PUT THE DETOX CLINIC ON ALERT.

"AFTER I PUT THIS COMIC UP, I GOT A LOT OF EMAILS FROM READERS OVERSEAS WHO INFORMED ME THAT THIS IS ACTUALLY A REAL BEVERAGE!

APPARENTLY MIXING BEER AND SODA IS VERY POPULAR IN BARS IN EUROPE, ESPECIALLY GERMANY."

"MAKING A MESS"

HI THERE. CAN I HELP YOU?
YEAH. I NEED YOU TO FIX MY COMPUTER. IT JUST STOPPED WORKING ALL OF A SUDDEN.
WHAT WERE YOU DOING WHEN IT STOPPED WORKING?
I WAS *ORGANIZING.*

COULD YOU BE MORE SPECIFIC?

WELL, I WAS LOOKING THROUGH THE "WINDOWS" FOLDER, AND I SAW THAT EVERYTHING WAS A MESS.

SO I DECIDED TO MAKE THINGS MORE TIDY. I MOVED ALL OF THE *.EXE* FILES INTO ONE FOLDER, AND ALL OF THE *.DLL* FILES INTO ANOTHER.

SO YOU'RE GONNA FIX IT, RIGHT?
HEY! WHERE DO YOU *THINK* YOU'RE GOING?
ON MY *LUNCH BREAK.* I'M NOT CERTIFIED TO DEAL WITH *THIS* PARTICULAR LEVEL OF *STUPIDITY.*

"YOUR WRITING WILL HAVE A DIRECT INFLUENCE ON THE TYPE OF AUDIENCE YOU ATTRACT. IF YOUR COMIC IS FULL OF JOKES ABOUT OBSCURE LINUX COMMAND LINES OR A D20 GAME PRODUCED AND SOLD ONLY IN NORTHERN SWEDEN, YOUR COMIC WILL APPEAL TO A VERY LIMITED GROUP OF PEOPLE.

ON THE FLIP SIDE, IF YOU MAKE A COMIC WITH VERY BASIC AND GENERAL HUMOR, WELL... THEN YOU'VE GOT A NEWSPAPER COMIC."

"DOWN IN FLAMES"

LUCAS, WE'VE BEEN GETTING SOME COMPLAINTS. COMP-U-WORLD PRIDES ITSELF ON OUR CUSTOMER SERVICE. WHAT SEEMS TO BE THE PROBLEM?
I'M TRYING, BUT YOU WOULDN'T BELIEVE SOME OF THE CUSTOMERS WE GET.
WE SELL THESE CHEAP, PRE-BUILT MACHINES WITH EVERYTHING INTEGRATED ON-BOARD.
WE THEN OFFER PILES OF STUPID REBATES AND CONTRACTS TO MAKE THEM SEEM EVEN CHEAPER...
AND IN TURN, WE ATTRACT EVERY REDNECK, CHEAPASS, AND COMPUTER IDIOT FROM A FIFTY MILE RADIUS WHO THINKS THEY'RE REALLY GETTING A HUNDRED DOLLAR COMPUTER...
WHO I THEN HAVE TO DEAL WITH AT THE TECH BENCH. ONLY RETARDS WOULD BUY AND USE THESE MACHINES.

I BOUGHT TWO OF THOSE COMPUTERS FOR MY KIDS.
UHH...
AND A FIND CHOICE YOU MADE! THOSE ARE SOME EXCELLENT COMPUTERS, WHICH IS WHAT I WAS GOING TO SAY NEXT!

YOU'RE FIRED.
"...AND THEN EVERY SINGLE ONE OF MY BRAIN CELLS CRIED OUT IN JOYFUL UNISON, THAT THEY WOULD BE SPARED FURTHER TORMENT AT THE HANDS OF THIS FUCKNUT-SATURATED ENVIRONMENT."

"I HATED THOSE STUPID UNIFORMS ANYWAY."

"NUCLEAR CRUSADER"

WELL, NOW YOU'VE DONE IT LUCAS. NOW YOU'RE UNEMPLOYED.

NOT THAT I REGRET IT, I GUESS. THAT PLACE SUCKED **BIG TIME,** AND THOSE CUSTOMERS WERE A PAIN IN THE ASS.

BUT STILL, I SHOULD HAVE MADE SURE I HAD ANOTHER JOB BEFORE RUNNING MY MOUTH LIKE THAT...

I'M SURE I COULD GET ANOTHER TECH JOB SOMEWHERE. THAT'S NOT REALLY THE PROBLEM.

I'M GOING TO RUN INTO THE SAME KIND OF IDIOTIC PEOPLE ANYWHERE I GO.

EVENTUALLY I'LL WIND UP RIGHT BACK HERE AGAIN.

OH WELL. I'M SURE I'LL FIND SOMETHING I CAN DEAL WITH.

IN THE MEANTIME, WE'VE STILL GOT SCOTT'S INCOME, AND IT DOESN'T SEEM LIKE ANYTHING IS GOING TO CAUSE ETHAN TO LOSE HIS JOB.

WE'LL BE OK.

MEANWHILE...
WHAT?! THERE WAS A FALLOUT 3 IN PRODUCTION AND NO ONE TOLD ME?!
AND NOW IT'S CANCELLED, AND NO ONE TOLD ME?!
THIS IS AN INJUSTICE WORTHY OF... OF... A CRUSADE!

"SHORTLY AFTER THIS FIASCO, IT WAS ANNOUNCED THAT PRODUCTION ON FALLOUT 3 WOULD RESUME UNDER THE HELM OF A NEW DEVELOPER."

"A PEACEFUL DEMONSTRATION"

SCOTT! I NEED YOUR HELP!
THAT'S A FRIGHTENING PROSPECT.
YOU KNOW A LOT ABOUT PROTESTING, RIGHT?
WHY DO YOU THINK THAT?

YOU KNOW... 'CAUSE. YOU'RE ALL... HIPPIE-CRUNCHY-TREE-HUGGY-SAVE-THE-WHALES AND STUFF.
YOU... WEAR SANDALS... AND STUFF.
HOW CAN I ARGUE, WHEN YOU PUT IT SO VERY ELOQUENTLY?

WHAT CAUSE ARE YOU PROTESTING FOR?
A GREAT, SINISTER EVIL IS BEING EXACTED ON VIDEO-GAMING-KIND! AND MOST OF THEM DON'T EVEN KNOW IT!
THEY MUST BE MADE AWARE! THEIR EYES MUST BE OPENED! OPENED!

SO... WHEN I ASSEMBLE MY PROTESTERS... DO THEY BRING THEIR OWN GUNS AND GRENADES AND STUFF, OR DO I HAVE TO SUPPLY THOSE?
YOU'RE THINKING OF MILITIA.
I JUST NEED TO BLOW STUFF UP!

"ONE OF THE DOWNSIDES OF RUNNING A BUSINESS AND AN EXTREMELY SUCCESSFUL WEBCOMIC IS THAT I HAVE LITTLE OR NO TIME FOR NON-CAD-RELATED PROJECTS. DURING THE LIFE SPAN OF CTRL+ALT+DEL, I HAVE STARTED NO LESS THAN SIX SECONDARY COMIC PROJECTS THAT NOBODY HAS EVER SEEN. I GET STARTED ON A NEW PROJECT, BUT THEN SOMETHING COMES UP WITH WORK AND REQUIRES ALL OF MY ATTENTION. CAD ALWAYS COMES FIRST, SO OTHER PROJECTS GET PUSHED TO THE BACK BURNER AND NEVER SEE THE LIGHT OF DAY."

"IN BATTLE?"

OH, HEY, ETHAN... UHH, I HAVE SOMETHING I NEED TO TELL YOU.
FALLOUT 3 WAS CANCELLED.
HUH? WAIT... WHAT DID YOU JUST SAY? OH SHIT...
HOW... HOW DID YOU FIND OUT?
WELL I'LL ADMIT IT WASN'T EASY, SINCE AT SOME POINT MY COMPUTER WAS FILTERED AGAINST ALL THINGS FALLOUT RELATED...
I'D BE PISSED AT A CERTAIN SOMEONE, BUT AT THE MOMENT THIS IS THE LEAST OF MY WORRIES. I HAVE A CRUSADE TO LEAD.
ETHAN, I JUST LOST MY JOB. YOU CAN'T TAKE OFF OF WORK NOW. WE NEED TO BE CAREFUL WITH OUR MONEY.
SORRY DUDE, THE CALL HAS BEEN MADE. I'VE POSTED ON THE INTERNET.
BY NOW THOUSANDS AND THOUSANDS OF GAMERS ARE PREPARING TO RALLY UNDER MY COMMAND AT INTERPLAY HEADQUARTERS TO FIGHT FOR OUR BELOVED GAME.
IF I SHOULD FALL IN BATTLE, KNOW THAT MY CAUSE WAS WORTHY, AND DO NOT WEEP FOR ME.
I'M CHANGING THE LOCKS AS SOON AS YOU LEAVE.

"ETHAN WILL OFTEN JUST UP AND DISAPPEAR FOR DAYS AT A TIME, BUT HE RARELY EVER DOES SO WITHOUT AT LEAST LEAVING ME A NOTE.

OR AT LEAST A MESSAGE ON THE BATHROOM MIRROR IN TOOTHPASTE AND MACARONI."

"THE JOB HUNT"

YES, HI. I'M CALLING ABOUT THE TECH JOB IN THE PAPER?
YES, A LOT OF PREVIOUS EXPERIENCE. YEP.
REASON FOR LEAVING? UHH...
I DIDN'T LIKE THE... SHIRTS?
YES, I'M CALLING ABOUT THE JOB IN THE PAPER.
I'M SORRY, I CAN'T HEAR YOU.
WHAT? NO, THERE'S A LOT OF BACKGROUND NOISE.
I'M SORRY, WHAT IS THAT?
ARE THOSE... GOATS?
YES, I'M A+ CERTIFIED. YES.
YES, I KNOW WHAT A HARD DRIVE IS.
YES, I KNOW WHAT A VIDEO CARD IS.
YOU KNOW, WE COULD JUST ESTABLISH THAT I HAVE A THIRD GRADE EDUCATION AND SKIP THESE QUESTIONS.
HELLO?
YES, ABOUT THE JOB...
WHAT?! NAKED? NO! WHAT DOES IT MATTER HOW BIG MY--
WAIT, I THINK I HAVE THE WRONG NUMBER. I'M LOOKING FOR A TECH JOB.
THIS IS A TECH JOB?!
NO! I DON'T CARE HOW GOOD THE TIPS ARE!

"I GOT ALL OF THE ARTISTIC TALENT IN THE FAMILY, AND MY YOUNGER SISTER GOT ALL OF THE MUSICAL TALENT. SHE IS A GRADUATE FROM THE BERKLEE COLLEGE OF MUSIC. I'M A GRADUATE OF.. NOWHERE.

NO, I'M JUST KIDDING. I GRADUATED FROM THE SCHOOL OF HARD KNOCKS...YO."

SNICKER

"HAM AND CHEESE"

OUTSIDE OF INTERPLAY HEADQUARTERS...
SO, YOU TWO MUST BE MY APPOINTED LIEUTENANTS.
WHERE ARE THE REST OF THE THOUSANDS? STRATEGICALLY PLACED ON SURROUNDING ROOFTOPS?
WE'RE ALL THERE IS.
Fallout

WHAT?!
WHAT!
THAT CAN'T BE! THEY... JUST HAVEN'T SHOWN UP YET. THEY'RE LATE.
YOU SAID TO MEET AT NOON. IT'S 2PM NOW. YOU ARE LATE.

HMM... WE'LL HAVE TO MAKE DO, THEN.
I HAD HOPED TO RELY ON A SHOW OF FORCE.
THE SECURITY GUARDS ARE ARMED. WE'RE GOING TO HAVE TO RUSH THEM.
SOME OF US MIGHT GET KILLED...

MY MOM PACKED ME A LUNCH.
OOPS. I JUST WET MYSELF.
IT'S HAM AND CHEESE.
YOU TWO BETTER STAY IN FRONT, WHERE IT'S SAFE.

"THE FALLOUT COMMUNITY IS PRETTY FANATICAL, AND I'M FAIRLY POSITIVE THAT IF A REAL CALL TO ARMS WAS MADE, YOU'D GET A LOT MORE THAN TWO CRUSADERS."

"LAST MAN STANDING"

WE NEED TO WAIT FOR THE MOST OPPORTUNE MOMENT...
THERE! HE BLINKED!
CHARGE!
RING! RING!

HI MOM. NO. NO. YES I ATE LUNCH. YES.
NO MOM. NO MOM.
OK MOM.

MY MOM SAYS IT'S GOING TO GET DARK SOON, AND THAT WE SHOULD COME HOME.
BUT, MY LINEAGE 2 BETA CD CAME IN THE MAIL! WANNA COME CHECK IT OUT, ETHAN?
WE CAN MAKE S'MORES!
KIND OF... CRUSADING HERE, GUYS.

"FIREPANTS! FIREPANTS!

...

IS IT LOGICAL TO BASE YOUR BRAIN ON CHEESE EXTRACT?"

"MYSTERY BOX"

INTERPLAY HAS ROBBED THE WORLD OF FALLOUT 3.
THE COMMUNITY HAS ABANDONED ME.
BUT THERE IS A CONTINGENCY. OH YES. A PLAN B.
IT'S DANGEROUS. MAYBE A LITTLE BIT CRAAAAZY. BUT IT JUST MIGHT WORK.

EXCUSE ME, MR. CAEN? THIS PACKAGE JUST ARRIVED FOR YOU. SAID IT WAS TO BE DELIVERED TO THE CEO OF INTERPLAY, IMMEDIATELY.
Corporate
FOR ME, HUH? OK, THANKS JIMMY.

PROBABLY MORE HATE MAIL...
Corporate
GIVE US BACK FALLOUT 3!!
rporate
CRACK!

"THE DOLL ETHAN IS HOLDING IS ICONIC FOR THE FALLOUT SERIES, KNOWN WIDELY AS THE MASCOT FOR THE IN-GAME PERSONAL DIGITAL ASSISTANT *PIP BOY.*

TO MY KNOWLEDGE, NO REAL PIP BOY DOLL EXISTS, BUT IF IT DID, I WOULD BUY ONE IN A HEARTBEAT."

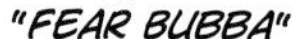

"DOING A WEBCOMIC FOR A LIVING HAS BEEN ONE OF THE MOST REWARDING AND FULFILLING EXPERIENCES OF MY LIFE, BUT RUNNING YOUR OWN BUSINESS IS BY NO MEANS AN EASY THING TO DO. THERE IS ABSOLUTELY NO JOB SECURITY IN THIS LINE OF WORK. I HAVE TO CONSTANTLY BE PLANNING FOR 'DOWN THE ROAD' AND WHAT'S AROUND THE CORNER.

PLUS THERE IS OFTEN A LOT OF BORING PAPERWORK THAT HAS TO BE DONE."

"MURDER ONE"

"ANOTHER REALITY OF RUNNING YOUR OWN BUSINESS IS THAT YOU DON'T REALLY GET SICK DAYS. YOU CAN'T CALL SOMEONE UP TO 'COVER YOUR SHIFT'. IF YOU'RE NOT DOING THE WORK YOURSELF, IT'S NOT GETTING DONE. IT CAN ALSO BE DIFFICULT, FOR ME AT LEAST, TO MAINTAIN REGULAR HOURS. OFTEN I FIND MYSELF JUST WORKING UNTIL I GET SOMETHING DONE, WHICH OFTEN MAKES FOR SOME VERY LONG DAYS."

"FULL REFUND"

LUCAS! YOU RESCUED ME! YOU'RE MY **HERO!**
I BAILED YOU OUT OF **JAIL**. IT WAS **EXPENSIVE**. YOU'RE PAYING ME BACK.

LUCKILY, INTERPLAY SAID THEY WON'T PRESS CHARGES. BUT YOU CAN ADD THEM TO YOUR LIST OF GAME COMPANIES WITH RESTRAINING ORDERS AGAINST YOU.
FINE. BUT IF THEY THINK THIS IS OVER, THEY ARE **SORELY** MISTAKEN. FALLOUT 3 **WILL** BE SAVED.

NOTHING WILL DISTRACT ME FROM MY--
OOOO! WHAT'S **THAT?** IT'S **SHINY!**
HEEERE, SHINY SHINY SHINY.

WHAT IS YOUR **RETURN POLICY?**
Administration

"NOT EVERYONE IS GOING TO LIKE YOUR COMIC. THE INTERNET IS CHOCK FULL OF PEOPLE WITH AN INFINITE VARIETY OF PERSONAL TASTES. THERE IS NO HUMANLY POSSIBLE WAY TO MAKE ALL OF THEM HAPPY. LISTEN TO CONSTRUCTIVE CRITICISM, BUT IGNORE UNINTELLIGENT, NEGATIVE INSULTS.

THEY AREN'T WORTH YOUR TIME. YOU'VE GOT BETTER THINGS TO DO, LIKE ENTERTAIN PEOPLE."

"NO SERVICE AREA"

...AND THAT'S ABOUT IT. WELCOME ABOARD!
DO YOU HAVE ANY QUESTIONS FOR ME?
NAH, I THINK I'M PRETTY FAMILIAR WITH THE ROUTINE.
YO, WAZZUP? YEAH, LISTEN. I NEED A NEW COMPUTER. I'M LIKE, THE BEST CALL OF DUTY PLAYER EVER, RIGHT?
BUT WITH ALL OF THE MAPHACKS AND AIMBOTS I RUN, MY COMPUTER IS GETTING A BIT SLOW.
SO UHH, YEAH. LIKE... WHICH ONE OF THESE COMPUTERS COMES WITH THE MOST FRAMES PER SECOND?
I'M SORRY, YOU MUST HAVE MISSED THE SIGN ON THE FRONT DOOR. "NO SHIRT, NO SHOES, NO BRAIN: NO SERVICE".
YO, MAN. DON'T FUCK WITH ME. I'M LIKE, A JUNIOR IN HIGH SCHOOL AND SHIT. THAT MEANS I'M TOUGH.
BUGGER OFF, BEFORE I GO GET YOUR MOTHER. I CAN SEE HER OUTSIDE IN THE MINI-VAN.
SORRY ABOUT THAT. I DON'T HAVE A VERY HIGH TOLERANCE FOR IGNORANCE.
WHAT?
WHY ARE YOU GRINNING LIKE THAT?
IT'S STARTING TO CREEP ME OUT...

"WELL, YOU GUYS HAVE SAT THROUGH ANOTHER BOOK FULL OF MY POINTLESS RAMBLING. THERE REALLY MUST BE SOMETHING WRONG WITH YOU. YOU MIGHT WANT TO GO SEE A PROFESSIONAL THERAPIST. MAYBE GET ON SOME MEDS.

AT ANY RATE, THANK YOU FOR READING THE SECOND COLLECTION OF CTRL+ALT+DEL COMICS. I HOPE YOU ENJOYED READING THEM AS MUCH AS I ENJOYED WRITING AND DRAWING THEM!"

Extra Content

The following section contains
a series of Ctrl+Alt+Del comic strips
that are exclusive to this book. They can
not be found published anywhere
else.

I have also included
the artwork from the now-discontinued
Ten Commandments poster, which originally
debuted at Otakon 2003.

HEY,
I JUST PICKED UP *DEUS EX 2* FOR THE XBO-- ERR... FOR 'YOU'.
WOO! BRING IT ON, BABY! I'LL PLAY THAT DISC LIKE SHE'S NEVER BEEN PLAYED BEFORE!
BUT... IT'S A BRAND NEW DISC. IT *HASN'T* EVER BEEN PLAYED BEFORE...

WOO! FIRE IT UP! WE'RE GOING TO ROCK TONIGHT! WOO! YEEEHAAWW!
OK, CALM DOWN A BIT, SPARKY.

WHAT THE--? "DISC LOAD ERROR"? WHAT IS THAT?
HUH?! WHAT?!

'SHOOTING BLANKS', ARE WE?
AUGH!

"IT'S REALLY WEIRD, BUT OFTEN WHEN I'M DRAWING FACIAL EXPRESSIONS FOR THE CHARACTERS, I'LL CATCH MYSELF ACTUALLY MIMICKING THE EXPRESSION I'M DRAWING.

IT'S STRANGE, BUT I GUESS IT HELPS ME REALLY CAPTURE THE EMOTIONS I'M LOOKING FOR WITH AN EXPRESSION."

I'M SORRY... DID YOU JUST SAY YOU'RE "IMPOTENT"?
I'M NOT THE XBOX I USED TO BE. I CAN'T PLAY ANY OF THE NEW GAMES.

HMM... YOU KNOW, COME TO THINK OF IT... YOU *WERE* BUILT FROM A FIRST GENERATION XBOX. I'VE HEARD THE DVD DRIVES IN THOSE HAVE PROBLEMS READING SOME OF THE DISCS THE NEWER GAMES ARE ON...

SO *YOU* DID THIS TO ME! I'LL TEAR YOUR MEATY APPENDAGES OFF AND BEAT YOU WITH THEM!

WE *COULD* JUST REPLACE YOUR DVD DRIVE...
YOU'D BETTER HOPE SO. FOR *YOUR* SAKE...

"THIS IS A PROBLEM I FACED WITH MY FIRST XBOX. FIRST GENERATION XBOXES WERE MANUFACTURED WITH DVD DRIVES THAT COULDN'T READ TO THE VERY EDGE OF A DISC.

THIS WASN'T A PROBLEM FOR EARLY GAMES BECAUSE NONE OF THEM USED A FULL DVD. BUT AS NEWER GAMES CAME OUT, AND WERE USING ALL OF THE DISC, THE OLD DVD DRIVES COULDN'T PLAY THEM."

SO LISTEN, BABY... ABOUT THE OTHER DAY... THAT'S NEVER HAPPENED TO ME BEFORE. I SWEAR!

I'VE TALKED TO SOMEONE ABOUT IT, AND HE THINKS WE CAN CORRECT THE PROBLEM FAIRLY EASILY...

DON'T YOU LOOK AT ME LIKE THAT! I'M TOLD THIS IS A *VERY* COMMON PROBLEM FOR FIRST GENERATION XBOXES, AND *NOTHING* TO BE ASHAMED OF!

"I'VE LEARNED TO TOLERATE THE XBOT... BUT SOMETIMES IT CAN BE PRETTY ANNOYING HAVING TO DEAL WITH A THINKING, MOVING CONSOLE.

IT'S NEVER WHERE YOU LEFT IT, AND IT ALWAYS HAS ITS OWN OPINIONS ABOUT WHAT GAMES TO PLAY.

MOST OF THE TIME I JUST WANT TO GO BUY A REGULAR, STATIONARY XBOX."

I'VE GOT THE NEW DVD DRIVE HERE. SHALL WE GET TO IT, THEN?
I'M HAVING SECOND THOUGHTS.
WHAT?! ABOUT WHAT?
WHAT IF SOMETHING GOES WRONG? WHAT IF I END UP WITHOUT A DVD DRIVE ALLTOGETHER? THEN I WON'T EVEN BE ABLE TO PLAY THE OLD GAMES!

I'D BE A FREAK OF NATURE.
RIGHT...
THIS IS GOING TO TAKE TEN MINUTES. IT'S A VERY SIMPLE PROCEDURE. A FEW SCREWS, A COUPLE OF CABLES AND WE'RE ALL DONE.
SO SHALL WE GET STARTED?
GULP

"HEY MAN, DON'T SPEAK ILL OF THE XBOT. HE'S THE BEST THING I EVER MADE. I NO LONGER HAVE TO GET UP TO CHANGE THE GAME DISCS. I JUST TELL HIM TO GET UP AND CHANGE HIS OWN DAMNED DISCS.

IF I CAN FIGURE OUT A WAY TO INSTALL A MINI-REFRIGERATOR IN HIM, HE'LL BE PERFECT."

OK, THIS IS IT. YOU'RE ALL HOOKED UP. SHALL WE GIVE IT A SHOT?
ALRIGHT, HERE GOES NOTHING...

C'MON BABY, C'MOOOON! PLEASE, PLEASE, PLEASE, PLEEEEAAAASSE, PLE--

TITLE SCREEN! YES! I'M BACK, BABY! WOOOOO!
THANK YOU, THANK YOU, THANK YOU!

WOOOO!
COULD YOU STOP DOING THAT SO I CAN PLAY MY GAME NOW?

"HUMAN ERADICATION MODE ACTIVATED..."

Ctrl*Alt*Del Presents
THE TEN COMMANDMENTS

I BRING TO THEE THY TEN COMMANDMENTS OF GAMING!

KNOW THY L337NESS!

I. Gaming is the Lord thy god, thou shalt not have outdoor activities before thee.

II. Thou shalt not take the name of halo in vain.

III. Remember thou keep holy the release dates.

IV. honor thy controller and thy console.

V. Thou shalt not frag.. without gloating in the aftermath.

VI. Thou shalt not bitch, nor whine when fragged.

VII. Thou shalt not kill steal.

VIII. Thou shalt not use aimbots or maphacks.

IX. Thou shalt not covet thy neighbor's rocket launcher.

X. Thou shalt not overclock without proper cooling.